The Beggar
King of China

The Beggar King of China

Dale
Carlson

illustrated by John Gretzer

Atheneum 1971 *New York*

For my mother and father,
Estelle and Edgar Bick

Contents

1690301

The Beggar
King of China

Foreword

THE STORY of the Beggar King, son of a poor farmer, leader of rebel bandits, and finally, in 1368, Emperor of all China, is like much of Chinese history—the story of peasant revolts against weak, cruel or corrupt emperors. In Europe, a king ruled by Divine Right. In China, the glorious "Son of Heaven" sat on the Dragon Throne only as long as he protected the nation from its two worst enemies, the barbarians and famine. If he failed, he was accused of being false to the Mandate of Heaven, and entire armies of peasant rebels rose up to place a new emperor on the throne. Since the time of Jesus Christ up to the twentieth-century Red Army, there have been peasant revolutions every few centuries in China. The leaders of the Red Chinese may have read the works of the Westerner Karl Marx, but they also knew their country's history. The peasant revolt is a tradition almost as old as China itself.

It was against these two enemies, barbarians and famine, that Chu Yuan-chang, whom men called the Beggar King, fought for nearly twenty years during the fourteenth cen-

3

tury. A hundred years before, the mounted Mongols of Genghis Khan's Golden Horde had crossed the Great Wall to conquer North China. His grandson Kublai succeeded in conquering South China, and from his capital in Peking, called Cambaluc by the Mongols, Kublai ruled all of China with the cruelty of a barbarian. Yet, because the Mongol Empire extended from China through Central Asia, Russia, and eastern Europe as far as the Danube River, Chinese merchants benefited from world trade. It was during the reign of the Khans that China taught Europe about moveable type, paper mills, and gunpowder.

At the same time, under Kublai and his corrupt successors, China suffered terribly from overtaxation, suppression, and starvation. Throughout China's history, the Mongols had ridden out of their deserts and grasslands to sack Chinese cities, but never before had any barbarian sat on the Dragon Throne.

The revolt against Mongol rule began in the south of China along the Yangtze River. In the beginning, separate rebel bands and secret societies, each with its own chief, attacked Mongol garrisons, but by 1351 (by Western dates, which I have used to avoid confusion), a band known as the Red Turbans found a great leader in young Chu Yuan-chang, and the rebels emerged into open rebellion. First South and then North China was recovered. The Mongols were driven back into Mongolia, and the army crowned Chu emperor.

This story, of the boy who began his life on the poorest of farms and ended it by founding one of the most brilliant dynasties in his country's history, is one of the great hero epics of China.

Dale Carlson

Breath of the Dragon

C HU YUAN-CHANG, waiting for death, stared
through the darkness across his father's rice fields
to the wintry hills. As he waited, crouched silently against
the thick, earthen walls of the house, Chu wondered which
form of death the Lord of Hell would take. Outlined in
the moonlight on the crest of a distant ridge, he saw four
Mongol horsemen. They would think nothing of killing a
family of Chinese farmers. Earlier, Chu had seen a band
of Chinese rebels. Bandit rebels killed as easily as the
Mongol soldiers.

Chu shivered in his quilted jacket and trousers. Cold
brought death. So did hunger. Today he had eaten only
some earth mixed with water and a handful of grass, and
they had long ago stripped and eaten the bark from the
trees. Yesterday, Chu's elder brother had died. His parents,
too, were dying. Death was everywhere along the Yangtze
River. Chu was not frightened. He was full of anger.

"Yuan-chang!"

The cry came from inside the house. It was his mother's voice.

Softly, through the small, square hole of a window, Chu answered her call.

"In a moment, mother."

The cloud he had prayed for to the Goddess of Mercy crossed the moon. A good omen. He prayed now that she would keep evil spirits from his path.

In the darkness, Chu crept noiselessly toward the narrow, raised path that separated the two small northern rice fields. The fields were muddy after yesterday's heavy fall of good rain—not that it mattered, since this year there was no new seed to plant. Chu crawled on, keeping close to the ground. A sharp rock cut his knee through a worn place in his trousers, but Chu dared not rise or cry out with the Mongols still on the ridge. At the end of the path, Chu reached the small mound that was the graveyard of his ancestors. Shaded by the branches of an apricot tree and enclosed by a wall of earth, this good place in the fields had been set aside by Chu's great-grandfather so that dead or alive the family would rest on their own land. Even in bad times, when every inch of land was precious, Chu remembered that his father had refused to use this ground for planting.

"It is the sign of an established family that it can afford to spare ground for its ancestors," Chu's father had said. "So far, we have not had to dig up our ancestors' bones and carry them on our backs."

Now it hurt Chu's heart to think how hard his father had tried to keep things going. Chu's father loved the land the way Chu loved the people who lived on it.

Chu listened and waited. But the stillness was broken

only by the wind in a nearby grove of bamboo. He crawled over the wall at the foot of the mound, and, careful not to step on the graves, walked to the small shrine of the Earth God under the apricot tree. He was afraid because of what he was going to do. It was one thing to defy death at the hands of Mongol soldiers and Chinese bandits; it was another to defy the gods.

But on the tiny shelf of the shrine, before the clay figure of the Earth God, was a small handful of beans. These last beans Chu's mother had given to the god as an offering for his protection against further disaster. There had been no help, no protection from the god. And now Chu wanted those beans. If he chewed them into a soft pulp first, his mother and father might be able to swallow a little and gain strength.

Fearfully, Chu stretched out his hand for the beans. His hand found nothing. He searched with his fingers behind and all around the Earth God's statue.

A sudden small noise, the barest scraping sound, spun Chu around just in time to defend himself from the smashing blow of a fist. There was no second in which to think whether the evil-smelling man in ragged clothes was a bandit or another poor, hungry farmer like himself. Chu flung all his weight against the intruder, and they both fell to the ground, grappling with each other and rolling down the hill. The earth wall encircling the grave-yard stopped their fall, and they struggled where they lay. Each tried to mount the other. As they clung together, Chu stared into the man's narrow, glittering eyes and understood the man meant him to die. Chu was weak from hunger, but he was tall and well-muscled for his seventeen years. Clearly, the other, though savage, was older and worn by his years. The matted hair and scraggled wisps of beard showed gray under the emerging light of the moon. The man got his hands free from Chu's grasp, and a moment later, they closed around his neck. In a furious burst of strength, Chu tore the hands loose, climbed astride his enemy, and brought down his fist, over and over again until the man lay still. Horrified, Chu leaped away. Panting for breath, he stared at the motionless intruder from a distance before he crept close again.

He saw two things at once.

The man was dead.

And it was he who had stolen the beans. They were in a small leather pouch hanging from the man's neck.

How terrible that the greatness of China had fallen to this, that one person should kill another for a handful of beans.

Chu's eyes scanned the ridge of the distant hills. The Mongol soldiers still rode the crest.

"It's your fault, you barbarian sons of pigs," Chu whispered in anger. "But only wait! One day there will be a Chinese Emperor, not a Mongol, on the Dragon Throne. And you will be beaten out of the Middle Kingdom back to the deserts you came from. You have no right to be here in the land of my ancestors, and I will not rest until you are gone."

Chu raised his fist against the heavens. If the gods heard, they gave no sign. There was only the sound of the Wind Dragon driving the clouds across the sky.

Chu hurried back to the house and entered the middle room. Once there had been a long red table and four square stools in the middle room, just as there had once been pigs and chickens and a water buffalo in the shed that leaned against the back of the house. The pigs and chickens they had eaten last month. The water buffalo and the furniture had been sold for rice.

Chu went quickly to the oven, made of earthen bricks as the house was, great squares of earth dug from their own fields. He looked into the iron pot on top of the oven. A few cups of water remained. Dipping a little of the water into his rice bowl, he took it into his parent's room.

They were lying together on the raised, brick *kang,* hollow to allow heat from the oven on the other side of the wall to warm them in their sleep. But there was no fuel left for heat. Only the rush matting beneath them and the thin quilt over them provided warmth. His mother seemed to be sleeping. His father, wasted and feverish, plucked at the quilting with shriveled, knotty fingers and stared through a hole in the thatched roof.

"There was rain enough yesterday to bring a crop to

fruit," said his father suddenly. "If the rice beds do not yellow and die this year and the taxes on our wheat and rice grow no greater, I will buy the piece of land near the village wall. It will be easy to water from the moat."

Chu knelt at his father's side.

"Yes, Father, and then to please my mother, we will plaster the inner walls of the house and whitewash the outside and perhaps even add a courtyard with more rooms to the back."

His father's mind often wandered now, to a past when times were better and there was still hope. His greatest comfort was in Chu's reassurance that nothing had changed. As his father continued to dream aloud, Chu put half of the beans into his mouth and ground them with his teeth until they were soft. With his fingers, he took the pulp from his own mouth and pushed it into his father's. His father gulped, swallowed, and began to cough. Chu held up his father's head and gave him some of the water.

"I am cold," his father complained. "I want a grandson to warm my bones. We cannot afford wedding costs, but I will buy a slave woman for your elder brother to give me my grandsons. Or perhaps the poor Hung family on the other side of the village will soon not be able to feed so many mouths and will sell me one of their daughters. Poor Hung. His rice bowl has been broken for a long time. And your elder brother, he wishes for sons."

Chu made no answer. Had his father forgotten the death of his eldest son? Chu glanced across the room. On the earth floor lay his brother's body, covered with straw.

His father coughed deeply and then suddenly began to speak in the harsh, normal voice Chu had quickly obeyed all of his life.

"When the devils of disease and hunger have had their

way with me and I go to join my ancestors, do not leave
the land. When the soldiers trample the rice shoots in the
fields, plant again. When they settle in the village and seize
a year's harvest, raise another crop. When the livestock
disappears with the soldiers, and in the wake of the
soldiers the bandits steal what is left, even then remain
on the land. Only in his land can a man find strength."

At the sound of the old argument, Chu grew hot with
anger. Always, everything had been sacrificed to keep the
land. Never were there comforts for his mother, schooling
for himself and his brother. Never was there a holiday
except for New Year's and the Spring and Autumn
Festivals. The land came first, according to the wishes of
his great-grandfather, his grandfather, and his father, who
underlined the importance of the land with the importance
of the teachings of Confucius.

"A good man follows the ways of his ancestors."

But Chu, as stubborn as his father, smoldered silently.
Before a Chinese farmer could follow the ways of his
ancestors, China must once again belong to the Chinese.
Chu had no intention of sitting on a piece of land, waiting
to die. Disobedience in a child was a terrible thing, but
Chu would find other ways to honor his ancestors, as the
great heroes of the past had done. Chu had often crept to
the village, in moments stolen from the fields, to listen to
the traveling storytellers. Like the strongest rice wine,
their tales of ancient heroes, the great Duke of Chou, the
Emperors of Ch'in and Han who built the Great Wall and
fought off the barbarian Tartars, intoxicated Chu and filled
him with a great passion for the destiny of his people.
Truly, he would count himself fortunate even to do one
small thing for the good of his oppressed land. How often
his father mocked him:

"Such an insignificant worm, and already he takes all of China on his shoulders."

This time, however, Chu kept his anger against the barbarians inside his heart. His father was dying, and it would be cruel and undutiful to argue with him now. His father's eyes were closed. He seemed to be sleeping peacefully. Chu left him to creep to his mother's side.

She looked small and very tired. Her tiny, bound feet, four inches in length, peeped out from beneath the quilt. Those feet, which had never been expected to walk farther than the distance of her own rooms, had followed her husband into the fields without complaint.

She took Chu's hand in her own.

"Yuan-chang," she said softly. It was all she need say to remind him that it was he she loved best in the world.

As he had done for his father, Chu took beans from the leather pouch and began to grind them. But when he wished to put the pulp in his mother's mouth, she closed her teeth firmly against his fingers. He understood instinctively that she was not refusing his act of filial piety, but that she could no longer swallow.

"My strength lives now in you," she whispered, her voice weaker than ever. "But where did you find food? And why is there blood on your hand? Did you not pray to the Goddess of Mercy to keep evil spirits from your path?"

"I have prayed to our ancestors' tablets; I have prayed to your favorite Buddhist Goddess of Mercy, Kuan Yin; I have prayed to the gods of the four directions and to those of Heaven and Earth, even to the Heavenly Jade Emperor of the Tao priests. They do not listen, Mother. They do not listen because a man must help himself before the gods can do anything in his behalf."

His mother raised a hand as a shield to her eyes. "O

Fountain of Wisdom, truly the brilliance of your words blinds me," she said with sarcasm. "He can barely read or write, this son of mine, but already he speaks as if he has memorized the Five Classics and the Four Books."

As always, Chu bore his mother's teasing with good grace. Though her husband and sons often smarted under her wit, they were proud to have a person in their family who could not only read and write many characters, but who had been brought up and educated in the city of Nanking. In a good year, his father had been able to afford the wedding costs and the presents of head ornaments, lengths of silk, and delicacies for the table. He had also found an able go-between who had managed to represent him as a prosperous landowner, not just a lowly farmer.

"All your life what I have most wanted for you was an education," said his mother. She was no longer teasing. Her whispering voice grew earnest. "Your elder brother would have been a good farmer. But there is something else in you, Yuan-chang, something passionate that will turn to violence one day unless your metal is tempered with knowledge."

Chu thought of the man he had killed. He would not worry his mother by telling her, but in some way she seemed to have guessed that there were things in his nature he did not yet understand.

His mother gripped Chu's hand more tightly. "Promise me you will leave Chung-li and go to the Buddhist monastery of Hua Shan. It lies within our province of Anhui, just south of the Yangtze River. They will teach you what you above all must learn: that to be a scholar is far more important, if you wish to serve China, than to be a fighter. We do not need another bandit rebel in the family like my brother Kuo Tsu-hsing." His mother paused, gasping for breath. "Promise me, Yuan-chang, that you will study hard to earn your degree so that you may become a government official. Even a poor man can rise to high position if he will work to pass his examinations. Promise, my son, promise you will go to the monastery."

"I will try," said Chu.

His mother smiled. "What you try, you will accomplish, child." Her eyes gazed about the room and rested momentarily on the dead body of her elder son. "No coffins for any of us," she said, her voice trembling. But she complained no further. He understood, and buried his face against her. When he raised his eyes once more, his mother was dead.

Half an hour later, his father died too, and Chu Yuan-chang was alone.

Chu went outside the house. An icy wind blew from the northeast, and the cold moon hung like a piece of broken silver lighting the dark amid gathering clouds.

"I cannot honor my parents with a worthy funeral," he thought. "I have no strings of cash to pay for coffins, and there is no one left for a procession." No gray-robed Buddhist monks with the nine sacred scars on their shaven heads would help these souls to join their ancestors. No yellow-robed Taoist priests would chant services of intercession from the sacred books. He had no paper money or houses or horses to burn. Not even a stick of incense. He could not wear the white sackcloth of mourning. All that was possible was to inscribe the names on soul tablets and to pray himself at the family altar in the niche by the stove.

Chu stared across the barren fields and saw the wind whip the branches of the apricot tree. It came to him that of all the farmers of Chung-li, only his ancestors rested on their own land. He understood now that this was honor enough.

It was a gift from the gods that the Mongol horsemen were gone. Throughout the rest of the night and into the morning, Chu dug the graves. He had only the two-pronged hoe his father had used to turn over the light soil of the rice fields. It worked slowly against the nearly frozen earth on the mound. Over and over again, Chu grasped the long handle in both hands to lift it above his head and bring it down against the earth.

The morning sun warmed him a little and a mouthful of grass kept him from fainting with hunger. When the graves were dug, he went back to the house and wrapped his parents and his brother in straw. Their thin bodies had almost no weight at all as Chu laid them in the ground. It was not until he had covered them over with the freshly dug soil and could no longer see their faces that he wept in violence and anger, as well as sorrow.

"Womanish tears," he mocked himself bitterly. "It is my strength that must honor them in death, not my weakness."

At midday he returned to the house. When he was small, in an hour left to him now and then between working in the fields and the forced labor of tending to a herd of Mongol cattle, Chu's mother had taught him to read and write nearly two hundred characters, some needing many strokes of the brush. He was pleased now to be able, by himself, to inscribe the three names on three pieces of wood and place them on the family altar. He kowtowed before the soul tablets and offered his prayers. Then he had done all he could. Even the Kitchen God could not carry a bad report of him to heaven at the New Year.

All that was left to do was to pack. Spreading his mother's carrying cloth on the ground, he placed in the middle their four rice bowls, four pairs of chopsticks, and the small, wooden hairpin his mother had worn when her silver ones had had to be sold. He would leave the cooking pot. It was heavy to carry, and he would have no use for it.

From the earthen doorsill of the house, Chu glanced across the land for the last time. Knowing what was to come, he had secretly made the arrangements, and in an hour the land would be sold to pay his father's debts. But still it was something to remember that in the moment of his burial, the soil of the mound had been his father's own. One day, if his efforts found favor in the judgment of the gods, Chu would come back for the bones.

Shivering under the graying sky, Chu started across the fields toward the south. A whiteness, rare in southern China, began to fall about Chu's head and shoulders in soft, powdery flakes.

"Snow!" breathed Chu softly to himself as he watched the white magic cover the hills and fields and trees. "Beautiful, like white jade," he thought. His mother had called it the wintry breath of the Dragon.

As everyone knew, Dragon's Breath was an omen of good fortune.

The Lord of Hell

I N T H E G R A Y L I G H T of dawn, Chu climbed the
great sacred mountain of Hua Shan. Fingers of mist
trailed across the pine slopes above him. But through the
silvered haze he could see the buildings of the monastery,
some of the outer ones nested against the mountainside and
the rest descending into the high mountain valley below.
He had come a long way, through the farms and marshes
and lakes of the Yangtze valley, through walled towns
and solitary mountain passes, across the wide Yangtze
River itself, begging, working for a few copper cash where
he could, and hiding from soldiers and bandits alike.

He was so thin that his bones showed clearly under his
skin, and so tired he could no longer fear. If he were
asked to sail to the Eastern Sea and steal from the blue sea
dragon the topmost horn on the crest on his back, or to
break a front tooth from the jaw of the tiger of the Hua

Shan Mountain, he would do it with a yawn. Not wood elves nor mountain ghosts nor wild rats nor fox spirits could make him so much as leap aside.

Doggedly he climbed on, until he reached the spacious halls, the soaring curved roofs, and the thick stone walls of the monastery. At the entrance gate, he sank down to rest before presenting himself to the Fang Chang.

He must have fallen asleep, because the sun was high and gold in the sky when he felt himself being shaken. A gray-robed monk with a thickly fleshed face under his shaven head stared down at Chu, in disgust and contempt.

"You are to follow me, miserable bag of bones," said the monk.

Anger rose in Chu as he thought for the thousandth time that the hearts of the well-fed were harder than the hearts of the gods.

Yet he had no choice but to bow and scramble to his feet. The monk took the edge of Chu's sleeve between his thumb and forefinger as if he were handling a thing inexpressibly vile, and led Chu through the entrance gate and across the outer court to the Hall of the Four Heavenly Kings. These must be like the Tao gods of the four directions his father had burned offerings to: the black tortoise of the north, the red bird of the south, the green dragon of the east, and the white tiger of the west.

"How alike religions are," he said aloud.

"Hold your worthless tongue," said the monk and led Chu across an inner court to the Great Main Hall, where, under the soaring rafters, dozens of gleaming bronze and lacquer statues, representing all the natures of Buddha and his disciples, lined the walls. In the center of the central hall was the vast image of Ti Tsang, Lord of Hell, Ruler of the Dead. It was he, who, loving mankind, had delayed entering the peace of nirvana that he might deliver souls from the torments of hell. Everywhere, incense and candles burned, and in the shrines were offerings of tea and rice. Somewhere, a service was in progress. Chu could hear the chanting of the sacred books and the sounds of bells, drums, and cymbals.

The monk led Chu on, naming in a self-important voice, for Chu's benefit, the monastery buildings they passed. There was the Hall of the Law, the library, the Hall for Meditation, and, along the sides of the courts of the large halls, countless cells for the monks, guestrooms, storerooms, and dining halls. Finally, toward the rear, they passed through a door in the wall, and crossed a flowered lawn. It was shaded with blue-green pines and edged with the paler silver-green of bamboo. In the shade of the pine woods was a small pavilion, surrounded by a verandah with beautifully carved marble railings.

"Wait here," said the monk and left Chu standing on marble steps near purple wisteria planted in a tub.

He returned a moment later to say, "Follow me. Unfortunately, the Fang Chang, our honored master, insists upon seeing every beggar personally, as an act of humility."

At a respectful distance, Chu followed the monk into the central chamber of the Fang Chang's dwelling. A long table and two armchairs were reflected in the polished stone floor. A portrait of the Goddess of Mercy hung on the wall. The room shone with cleanliness. Standing before a small altar, the Fang Chang smiled and greeted Chu kindly.

"Wan fu," said the head of the monastery. "Ten thousand happinesses."

Chu dropped to his knees and kowtowed three times, overcome by the kindness in the voice of one so great as the Abbot of the Hua Shan monastery toward such a small person as himself.

"Please rise," said the Fang Chang gently, and then in a sharper voice said to the monk, "Bring food."

Chu struggled to his feet.

"Be seated," said the Fang Chang, sitting in one chair and motioning Chu to be seated in the other.

But Chu heard his mother's words in his head. "Never sit in the presence of your superiors. Even when you are invited, think twice."

Chu remained on his feet, eyes cast down politely.

The Fang Chang noted Chu's behavior approvingly.

"Who are you?" said the Fang Chang.

"I am a son of the house of Chu from the village of Chung-li, with the personal name of Yuan-chang, Ancient and Honored Sir."

"You have traveled a long way," said the Fang Chang. "And how many springs have you counted?"

"I have squandered seventeen worthless years, Ancient One," Chu answered politely.

"The son of a farmer?"

How did the Fang Chang know that? Chu chanced a quick look at the tall, elderly figure with the fine, intelligent expression, which even the youngest Chinese learn early to associate with scholars versed in the Classic Wisdom. From beneath the sleeves of the Fang Chang's orange silk robe, his hands, held carefully within each other, boasted nails three inches long. It was the sign that their owner did no manual labor. Chu examined his own enlarged, coarse hands with their broken, blackened nails. It took no great feat of mind, Chu supposed, to see that he could be nothing but the son of a farmer.

"Do not feel shame at so worthy an occupation," the

Fang Chang rebuked Chu. "Do you not know that the wise Confucius taught that in virtue farmers are above artisans, merchants, and soldiers, and that they rank second only to the scholar?"

"I know nothing," answered Chu humbly. "That is the reason I have come to Hua Shan."

The Fang Chang looked surprised and seemed about to ask a question when the thickly fleshed monk came in and placed a small bucket of steaming rice, a dish of shredded pork and vegetables, a bowl and a pair of chopsticks on the table.

"You must sit now. Eat and gain a little strength," said the Fang Chang.

Chu sat only on the edge of the chair. He filled his bowl quickly and, picking it up in his hands, turned his body so the Fang Chang need not watch him chewing. His face burned with embarrassment because of his hunger and because it might be his manners were coarse. The Fang Chang rose.

"Some exquisitely shaped rocks have been sent to me for my garden," he said. "I will see to their placement and return in a few moments."

Chu ate as fast as he could two bowls of rice and two of the meat and vegetables. He had not seen such food in a year.

When he had finished, the Fang Chang returned.

"Tell me now, your reasons for coming to Hua Shan," said the Fang Chang. "Was it perhaps on the advice of a fortune-teller who read your destiny from the Eight Trigrams?"

Chu kept his glance on the polished floor. If he spoke the truth, would he be accepted here? But if he did not speak the truth, surely the Venerable Master would know.

Chu stood up so as not to sit in the Ancient One's presence. But this time, without thinking, he looked boldly into the Fang Chang's eyes.

"I have come for knowledge because I want to fight the Mongol barbarians. But I do not want to fight in the manner of my Uncle Kuo and the other rebel bandits who destroy as much of China as the Mongols do. By studying, I hope to learn how this may best be done."

"I see," said the Fang Chang quietly. He lit a tiny water pipe, took two puffs, and laid the pipe into a small dish. "You wish to kill without killing. Is that it?"

"I don't want to kill at all," said Chu stubbornly, "but I don't think the Mongols will ride the Wind Dragon's back out of China simply for the asking." He thought of the man who had stolen his mother's offering of beans from the Earth God's altar. "Sometimes it is necessary to fight for one's life. Or for someone else's. I have listened to the storytellers and the travelers who came to our village, and I have seen many things for myself. The Mongols tax the peasants until they starve; and what they do not tax, they take. Chinese men may not even have arms to protect themselves." Fury darkened Chu's eyes, and his fists clenched.

"Nor are the Chinese any longer given high official positions even when they take first place in the examinations. On the farms and in the walled cities, the door of each house must list all those who live within, so that not one of us may escape their lists. And do you know why they keep such lists? Even now the Mongol Emperor, Toghan Timur, to satisfy his lust for pleasure and his greed, is planning to carry out the suggestion of his ancestor Genghis Khan—to exterminate the Chinese and seize their property. Not that he plans to kill us all. No," Chu stormed, "only those named Chang, Wang, Liu, Li, and Chow."

"We have not many family names in China," said the Fang Chang, with a smile. "To kill all people with those names would be to take the lives of nine-tenths of China."

"Exactly," said Chu, nodding. "And do you know what he has lately done?"

"Tell me," said the Fang Chang, plucking a flower from vines that had been trained over the bamboo latticework of a window.

The calm detachment of the Fang Chang only served to increase the passionate anger in Chu's heart. That was the trouble with so many of the scholar class. They spent too much time celebrating the beauty of wind and water and rocks and flowers, and too little time on people.

"Well, speak," prodded the Fang Chang gently. "Tell me what the Emperor has done."

"He has taken so much money from the people of North China that there is a famine," Chu began angrily. "But will he give any of the money back? No. He has spent it all on his dancing girls and on the parks of Cambaluc. He has had a dragon-ship made to sail the waters of his park, which nods its head, wags its tail, and paddles with its feet. This, while the Chinese starve. China will die without the Mongols having to lift their swords if we do not fight back soon. I have heard," said Chu in confidence, "that there are secret societies, especially a sect called the White Lotus, that are beginning to organize things better, so that all China will soon be in rebellion. The White Lotus is a Buddhist sect, Venerable One. Have you heard of it?"

"I have heard altogether enough of these matters for today," the Fang Chang said, his tone suddenly rather sharp.

Chu heard the Fang Chang's tone and was ashamed.

"I have been rude, Ancient, to talk so long about things you must know more about than my stupid self," he apologized. "I am still full of anger after the death of my family." And he told the Fang Chang how his parents and his elder brother had died. "My father wanted me to stay on the land, but I couldn't do that. I promised my mother I would try to come to Hua Shan. She said that to be a scholar was a more important way to help China than to fight."

The Fang Chang stirred in his chair and refolded his hands. "Does that empty head house any learning at all?" he inquired drily.

"My mother, who was born and educated in the city of Nanking, taught me in the hours my father could spare me from the land," said Chu. "I can read and write nearly two hundred characters, some needing many strokes of the brush."

"A Fountain of Wisdom!" sighed the Fang Chang, the very words Chu's mother had used when Chu crowed too proudly. "He knows two hundred out of the necessary four thousand and possible six thousand characters. Good. That leaves three thousand eight hundred characters you must learn before you can learn anything."

The Fang Chang heard Chu's gasp.

"A year's work, no more, if you are diligent in your practice," said the Fang Chang.

"I didn't make that sound because I fear the work," said Chu. "I made it because I suddenly understood that I was accepted." Chu bowed gratefully to the Fang Chang. He would work his eyes and fingers through all the watches of the night for this kindly, wise old man. Chu remembered how his father, brought up in the ways of strict Confucianism, used the Tao priests and Buddhist monks for marriage ceremonies, to exorcise bad devils, and to bury his dead, yet held them in contempt. This, because they did not marry and rear children to do reverence to ancestors, which was the highest duty under Heaven. Yet the Fang Chang was a great master. Surely even Chu's father would have respected him.

The Fang Chang clapped his hands, and the thickly fleshed monk appeared.

"I want you to take Chu Yuan-chang to the sleeping rooms and find him a bed. Tomorrow he will take the ten primary vows and enter our brotherhood as a novice."

"Vows?" said Chu, startled.

"You do not think you might refrain from lying, stealing, murdering, drinking wine, and bedding with singsong girls while you are with us?" the Fang Chang asked with a smile.

Chu blushed.

"Do not worry. Your first vows do not mean you are chained to us for life," said the Fang Chang. He turned again to his assistant. "Chu's religious instruction, the memorizing of sacred texts and the learning of our services, I will entrust to Brother Li. His formal education I will attend to myself. You will bring him to me every day after morning rice."

The fleshy monk led Chu back through the courts and halls to the row of sleeping rooms near the Hall for Meditation.

"Here," said the monk. He opened a door at the end of the row and motioned Chu to enter, moving aside to indicate that he did not wish so filthy a thing as Chu even to brush his garments. Were all monks so sullen and proud? Or had he made his first enemy? "I will have water brought, and fresh garments." Then he added, and it sounded more like a threat than an introduction, "My name is Brother Wang."

Chu forgot his worry over Brother Wang as he entered his room. It was whitewashed over good clean clay, and there were no holes in the walls for prying eyes or rats to enter. The window with its bamboo blind admitted a good light, and for furniture there was bed matting with a quilt and a small table and stool. Best of all, the room was his own. For the first time in his life, he need not share his sleeping place.

The door banged open. A small, slightly built boy of about Chu's own age struggled backwards into Chu's cell. He was so slender he seemed to drown in his gray novice's robe, yet he carried another like it over his arm and at the same time tried to pull a heavy bucket of water across the stone doorsill.

"Let me do it for you," said Chu.

"Please don't put yourself out," said the boy, but he stepped aside and gratefully accepted Chu's help. *"Aiya!* You are so large, and your hands and feet as well," said the boy, turning to examine Chu with friendly curiosity.

Chu had always been self-conscious about his height and his large frame. To him they were signs of country-bred coarseness, as was his broad, square-jawed face.

"With more flesh on your bones, it will take the strength of a thousand-pound water buffalo to deal with you," said the boy. Clearly there was admiration, not criticism, in his look, and Chu could not take offense. "And if the rumor is true, you have cleverness of mind as well."

"What rumor?"

"It is said the Master himself will teach you. He does that only for those he thinks worthy to prepare for the two great learned professions, the Buddhist priesthood or

service of the state. Which are you to be? A priest? Or will
you take the three Imperial examinations and become a
chin shih?"

Chu hardly thought of himself as becoming a mandarin
of the third degree, but he avoided the question by saying,
"Rumor travels quickly here."

The boy was too polite to pry further. "Yes, one must
be careful. It is a large community, yet everyone seems
to know everyone else's business."

"Who is Brother Wang?" Chu asked, keeping his voice
casual.

A shadow darkened the boy's face. "He serves the Fang
Chang personally and is jealous of his position. If you are
wise, you will stay clear of his path."

"Thank you for the warning," said Chu. "May I know
your name?" he asked politely.

"My family name is Hsu, and I have the personal name
of Ta."

"Thank you, Hsu Ta, for bringing my water."

Hsu Ta made the three customary bows and went to
the door. "I will return when it is time for evening rice,"
he said. "You must not expect partridge cooked with apricots here, but at least the Mongols have not yet broken
our rice bowls."

It had been fully a year since Chu had been able to wash
himself all over at one time. When he had finished washing,
he wiped his gums clean with the washing cloth and put
on the fresh robe. Not wanting to wrinkle the robe, he
sat carefully down on the stool to wait for Hsu Ta to come.
It was the first time in Chu's life that there was a space
with no work for his hands to do or miles for his feet to
travel. It was a strange and lonely feeling. But at least
there was time to think again about the future great rebel-

lion of all China against the Mongol rule, about how the people of the Middle Kingdom must be stirred to fight, not simply to accept their misery as the will of the gods.

"If only I could make everyone as angry as I," he thought, and then wondered, as he always wondered, how such an insignificant one as himself had so little humility to think he could help change the destiny of China.

At dinner Chu faced the torment with which all new novices were greeted. Without acknowledging his presence, the others at his table began to discuss the offensiveness of those fresh from the country.

"Countrymen are so stupid."

"Yes, but there are worse things than that about them. For instance, the way they smell of manure."

"Even that can be forgiven. It is the way they look I find so hard to bear, with such huge hands and feet and so much length in their bodies."

One remark followed another, until even the men at nearby tables began to laugh and top each other's quips at Chu's expense. The worst of the remarks were made by Brother Wang, who spoke seldom but to the point.

This time, though he burned with shame and anger, Chu knew better than to boast of his two hundred characters. He sat in silence and concentrated on forcing the hot rice down his throat.

"Look how he marvels at the number of tea leaves in his bowl," said Brother Wang. "It must seem to him feast enough for the Emperor himself."

"My father too was a farmer and so, I think, was yours, Brother Wang," a mischievous voice rang out from somewhere in the room. "But we all find it safer from bandits and soldiers behind these walls than in the open fields."

The words were delivered too rapidly for Brother Wang

to determine their source, and if he ever found out, the speaker's life would not be worth a single cash. But Chu knew who had spoken. It was Hsu Ta. Though so small a person, he had the courage of a tiger, and Chu would forget neither the courage nor the loyalty that had inspired it.

The next morning after rice, Chu found his way back through the great halls and courts to the Fang Chang's pavilion. Brother Wang greeted him coldly and led him through the central chamber to a library beyond. The Fang Chang sat at his table surrounded by more books than Chu ever imagined existed.

"Why do you look so amazed?" said the Fang Chang, smiling. "For more than two thousand years, the Chinese have been thinking and writing down their thoughts. And now it is your turn," added the Fang Chang with sarcasm, "to add to the wealth of the ages and the wisdom of the ancients. Sit down."

Under Chu's watchful eyes, the Fang Chang picked up one of two brushes lying on the table. He moistened it, rolled the hairs into a fine point on the slab of scented ink, and began to write on a thin sheet of paper.

"We will begin from the beginning, as you would in any ordinary village school, with the first sentence of the Three-Character-Classic. 'At birth, men are by nature good of heart.' "

How often Chu had heard the sons of those able to send their children to school chanting such recitations aloud as he herded cattle through the street. It was his turn to learn now, and he would make the most of it. Carefully he took the second brush and copied the characters as best he could. In the long hours of this first lesson, the Fang Chang mingled words of encouragement and criticism until it was time for noon rice.

"The afternoons we will devote to history and philosophy," said the Fang Chang. "And in the evenings you will perform whatever chores Brother Wang sees fit to give you."

"May I just hear some of the names of the sages and the great dynasties I am to study?" Chu asked.

"Bear in mind only the great names of Confucius, who taught us *li,* that is to order ourselves and society with proper behavior, and Lao Tzu, the Taoist sage, who said 'Do nothing and all things will be done.' They lived two thousand years ago during the Chou dynasty. As for the great dynasties, after the Chou came Ch'in, who first made an empire of China and built the Great Wall, then Han to expand our boundaries, and later the cultural ages of the Tang and Sung."

Like bronze gongs ringing down through the ages, the names and glories of the great houses of China echoed in Chu's mind—Chou, Ch'in, Han, Tang, Sung.

"And then came the Mongols," said Chu. Bitterness clouded his face.

"Always your thoughts return to the Tartars," sighed the Fang Chang. "Shall I teach the Ancient Wisdom to one who only wishes to use it for war?"

"But after war, will there not be a need for learning? China must be put together again and governed by our own mandarins."

The Fang Chang peered at him intently, then smiled and said, "You haven't yet written your first composition, and already you make plans for the future of the Middle Kingdom. Go now to eat noon rice, and find time on your way to pray to the gods for humility."

Chu fell to his knees and knocked his head three times

on the tiled floor of the library. "Forgive me," he said humbly. "I have much to learn."

But on his way through the Great Main Hall, Chu burned incense before the Lord of Hell. "As you save souls from the underworld," whispered Chu, "find me a way to help save China."

In the dining hall, Chu searched for Hsu Ta. When he could not find his small friend, he went to Hsu Ta's cell. Hsu Ta was lying on his bed, his robe pulled down to reveal the cutting strokes of a bamboo whip. Brother Wang's spies had found the source of yesterday's remark.

"I will make Brother Wang pay for this one day," Chu said angrily.

"Does your anger on my behalf mean you care enough to let me be your friend?" asked Hsu Ta, raising his head from the rush matting of his bed. He smiled at Chu through his hurt. "In that case, I will always be grateful to Brother Wang."

Mongol Devils

FOR MORE than two years, Chu studied at the monastery under the patient Fang Chang. Often, when Chu's mind was too full to memorize more texts or he felt shut in behind the high compound walls, he would roam the mountains to relieve the cramped sensation in his mind and legs.

"The mountains of China are beautiful, don't you think?" said Chu, his eyes shining, as he stretched his long arms upward as if to encompass the loveliness of the pines against the sky. "Why don't you answer me? Say something, Hsu Ta."

"You walk too fast," said Hsu Ta, panting for breath. But his complaint seemed a happy one. Chu knew his small friend enjoyed their walks together.

"I'm sorry," said Chu, smiling down.

"It's not your fault. It's just that you've grown again.

Your legs have gotten even longer. Look at your robe."

Chu looked down at his feet in straw sandals far too small for him. He saw that once again his robe was well above his ankles.

"I'll restitch it for you and make it longer," said Hsu Ta.

"No need," said Chu, laughing. "I'll only outgrow it again."

They came through the mountain mists to a high gorge, where a narrow waterfall cascaded down the rocks to foam in a pool below. Often they sat here together on the rocks that edged the pool, in the shade of the pines and the cassia trees. Always Chu sat silent for a while, and then he spoke to Hsu Ta of the things he was learning. On this day, early in spring, Chu had begun by reciting a poem by Li Po. It ended with words from the sacred *Tao te ching,* the Book of the Way of the Gods.

> Know therefore that the sword is a cursed thing
> Which the wise man uses only if he must.

"Then you still think of fighting the Mongols?" asked Hsu Ta. "I should have thought that after studying so long under the Fang Chang, your only concerns would be the perfection of your moral virtue and your literary style."

Chu turned sharply to see if Hsu Ta really so misunderstood him. But there was laughter in Hsu Ta's eyes. He was only teasing.

Chu's sharp look softened into a smile. "Even Confucius taught us that an Emperor must set a good example to his people to maintain harmony in the universe. And Mencius his pupil taught that if a ruler does wrong, Heaven withdraws its Mandate so that a better man may sit on the Dragon Throne."

"You know enough already to earn the Imperial degree of *chin shih,*" said Hsu Ta in admiration. "You will become an official and live in a great house and own land."

"I am my father's son, a peasant. I want no such honors," said Chu roughly. "I study only to understand better what I must do, and why." 1690301

"Don't be angry with me," said Hsu Ta. "Come," he added, jumping to his feet and brushing the twigs and leaves from his robe, "let's go to the clearing, and I will give you another lesson in swordsmanship."

The brooding darkness cleared instantly from Chu's eyes, and he sprang from his seat on the rocks to hurry ahead of Hsu Ta up the mountain path. Hsu Ta had once lived among monks who, like Brother Wang, belonged to the secret White Lotus sect, the Buddhists who collected and hid arms and taught their monks to fight, against the day when the Chinese people would rise up and drive out the barbarians. When Chu had discovered that Hsu Ta could use a sword, the lessons had begun almost at once. Now they were a joke. Chu far excelled his small master, when they practiced with the sticks as substitute for swords.

"You could make peace with Brother Wang by telling him you wished to join the White Lotus sect," Hsu Ta had once suggested. "He would be grateful for one who uses a sword as you do."

"I am not ready yet to join a rebel group," Chu replied. "And when I do, it will not be through Brother Wang. I do not trust him. He seeks power only for himself."

"He grows more jealous daily of the favor the Master bestows on you," Hsu Ta said.

"That is Brother Wang's problem," Chu answered shortly. "I will not fawn for friendship from a man like Brother Wang."

As they climbed now toward the clearing, Chu saw that as usual Hsu Ta looked to the left and right, peering constantly all around him and listening for sounds that were neither birdsong nor the rustling of wind in the bamboo. It was the difference between them, Chu thought, that while both were courageous, Hsu Ta was also careful.

"Are you watching for tigers or evil spirits?" asked Chu mockingly.

"Devils are devils. They come in many forms. They may even take the shape of leaves driven before the wind, or lurk in rivers and mountains and stones. A soothsayer came to the Eastern Gate this morning to decide on a fortunate location for a new pagoda. I took the opportunity to tell him the year, month, and day of your birth, and he said that today was not a lucky day for you."

Chu laughed. He no longer really believed in fortune-telling and superstitions. But when they came to the clearing, his large fist tightened on the stick he kept hidden there for sword practice. Certainly it would do no harm to be careful for once.

They began to wield their mock swords, Hsu Ta with deft, swift strokes to make up for his smallness, Chu with the balanced, powerful lunges of the tall and strong. Suddenly, without meaning to, he delivered a sharp blow to Hsu Ta's shoulder. He had counted on Hsu Ta to dart aside with his usual quickness. But something had caught Hsu Ta's attention. He stood absolutely still, his hand raised to make Chu silent, straining to hear something that Chu could not yet hear.

A moment later, Chu heard it too.

"The Tiger of Hua Shan Mountain," whispered Hsu Ta, naming his greatest terror and growing pale.

Chu shook his head. He had heard the sound before

many times and he knew exactly what it was. "Worse devils exist than the *kuei* of fallen leaves and tigers." Quickly he led the way through the clearing to the top of the mountain and pointed, through a space in the hovering mist, down the other side. "Mongol devils are worse. And they are coming to Hua Shan."

The sight of the horsemen as they rode silently in single file up the mountain made Chu tremble with anger. He stared at them for a long moment, noticing in detail their leather armor and helmets and the weapons they carried. Each held a scimitar or a battle-ax or a lance. All had lassos, bows, and two quivers apiece of arrows. Chu counted fifteen in the detachment altogether, no doubt from one of the garrisons stationed along the Yangtze River. What did they want from the Hua Shan monastery?

"We must warn the Fang Chang," said Chu in a low, angry voice.

"Yes, But don't expect him to fight," Hsu Ta whispered back. "It is something he will not do."

They arrived at the monastery only minutes ahead of the Mongol troops. Leaving Hsu Ta to warn the others, Chu raced through the halls and courts to the Fang Chang's pavilion. The Fang Chang was sitting in his garden, watching the silvery flash of fish in his lotus pool.

"They are here. The barbarians will ride through our gates in a matter of moments."

"You have not yet greeted me properly. Nor have you noticed that my peonies have begun to bloom," said the Fang Chang calmly. He continued to sit in his usual motionless manner in his lacquered chair by the pool, entirely ignoring the trembling anger in his pupil.

"Good afternoon, Old Gentleman," Chu said quickly, knowing that he would get no further without obeying the rules of courtesy. "Are there arms hidden anywhere in the monastery?"

"You know the Emperor Toghan Timur issued an imperial edict forbidding arms to the Chinese."

"Then I must capture a sword," said Chu.

"I forbid you to fight," said the Fang Chang. His silvery tone was cool and firm. As he spoke, Brother Wang appeared, his thick face an expressionless mask. He looked at Chu once, with cold eyes, and bowed to his superior.

"Your orders, Venerable?"

"You will open the gates," said the Fang Chang. "We will do nothing. Nothing at all."

If Brother Wang had any feelings in the matter, he showed none of them. He bowed again and left.

"For thousands of years, the barbarians have swept across our borders. Living among us long enough, they grow civilized. It is better simply to go on as we are, to teach rather than resist," said the Fang Chang to Chu, paying his pupil the compliment of an explanation.

Screams from the outer courts cut off any further argument.

Chu raced from the Fang Chang's presence back through the Great Main Hall. Before him, in the open court, several of the Mongol horsemen had lassoed a number of monks and were dragging them across the stones. Hundreds of other monks had been assembled to watch.

"You see how you will be treated if you do not give us your rice and silver," shouted a soldier, waving his curved sword.

"And we do not hesitate to kill," cried another. As his horse snorted and reared onto its hind legs, the Mongol waved a long leather thong. Attached to the thong were human ears, which the Mongol had cut off those he had killed in the past. "You," cried the Mongol, pointing to a novice in the corner of the court, "come here." As he spoke he let out his lasso and began to swing the loop in circles above his head. As he prepared to throw the loop, Chu glanced at the novice's face. It was Hsu Ta.

Chu moved quickly. Springing to the side of a Mongol whose attention was on the lasso, Chu dragged him from his horse and pulled the sword from his hand. Darting between the jostling horses, Chu reached Hsu Ta just as the loop passed over his head and tightened around his neck. Chu slashed the rope and spun immediately around to face attack, his sword arm raised in defiance. He was not permitted to fight. As if by accident the gathered monks began to push and jostle against each other until Chu and Hsu Ta were surrounded and hurried into the back ranks.

"Leave," they all whispered, one after another. "Leave before your rash acts get us all killed."

"You can still get out by the Northern Gate, if you are careful. Take Hsu Ta and go, or we will all be punished for what you have done." It was the cold voice of Brother Wang. Chu obeyed it.

The Middle Kingdom

U ND E R T HE H I G H southeastern wall of the great twelve-gated city of Hangchow, on the sandbanks of the Chientang River, huddled the makeshift huts of beggars, vagabonds, and starving peasant families driven south by the famine in the north. A small fire flickered before a mat shed. Around the fire, four beggars sat eating their evening meal of rice and pork. Charity, in strings of copper cash and pieces of broken silver, had been easy to beg that day. It was April 5th, the Festival of the Dead. After the festivities of the New Year in February and the Feast of the Lanterns, the Festival of the Dead was the city's most elaborately celebrated holiday.

"Come now," said the beggar named One Eye, whose only honesty was that in truth he had but one eye. "In return for our teaching you the best ways to earn evening rice, tell us more of your travels."

Chu had had enough of the Hangchow Beggar's Guild. These hideous, flapping bundles of filth and tatters who put thin knife blades under their flesh to draw blood for pity, who used their crutches for weapons to beat alms out of lepers, and whose only language was a whine or a curse, filled him with disgust. But it was also true that the evening before Hsu Ta had fainted from lack of food under the arch of the Great Eastern Gate, and this beggar, One Eye, and his grotesquely twisted companion had given Chu and Hsu Ta food and a sleeping mat. The companion, it turned out, was twisted not by nature, but by a complicated brace of leather straps in which he whined all day but which he removed at night.

Chu finished his pork and rice. There had also been fish, leeks, noodles, bamboo shoots, and even a cup of rice wine. Already Hsu Ta looked stronger, and Chu felt the energy return to his big frame. So, if these beggars were truly interested in what he and Hsu Ta had seen of China, he would tell them.

"In the two years we have traveled, we have been inland along the Yangtze River, which divides the Middle Kingdom in half like a great serpent. We went as far as the central provinces of Hupeh and Hunan, but not so far west as the frozen Himalayas of Tibet. We have gone north as far as the Yellow River, but not so far north as Peking, which the Mongols call Cambaluc, or the Great Wall or the Mongolian grasslands beyond. We have gone south to the province of Kiangsi, but not so far south as Canton, and to the east we have seen Shanghai and the Eastern Sea." Chu's slow, deep voice cast a spell on his listeners as he spread their vast and glorious country before them. He had been happy traveling, seeing and learning as much as he could of his country and his people. "And yet," Chu

went on, "though I do not wish to admire them, the Mongols have stretched their conquests, and therefore the empire we are part of, even beyond this. Under Genghis Khan and his grandson Kublai, the Mongols have devoured not only China but Central Asia, Russia, and eastern Europe as far as the Danube River."

"I care not what goes on in the north of China or in western lands," grumbled One Eye. "I know only that the old Beggar King, the head of our Guild, says that seventy-five years ago Hangchow was the capital of China. The Sung Emperors sat on the Celestial Throne in the Imperial Palace just behind this wall." Beggar One Eye jerked a thumb in the direction of the southeastern ramparts. "The Beggar King says even beggars were rich in those days. But tell me," said One Eye curiously, "wasn't it dangerous traveling along the Yangtze River? I hear that in the river marshes and among the lakes there are many chieftains whose men are half-rebel, half-bandit, and that while they kill Mongols when they can, they kill each other and everyone else who crosses their path as well."

"What you say is true," answered Chu, throwing more twigs on the fire from the nearby pile.

One Eye stared narrowly at Chu. "Then why do you still live?"

Chu understood the thought in the beggar's mind at once. If the two of them had survived, was it not possibly because they were bandits themselves? And if this was true, the beggar could earn paper money or even a bar of silver by reporting them to the police at the yamen. They might be thrown into jail with iron collars around their necks, or even tortured to death, since they had no money to buy freedom. Chu hastened to reply, but Hsu Ta was ahead of him.

"Everywhere we went we consulted fortune-tellers and traveled only on lucky calendar days," said Hsu Ta.

Beggars were a superstitious lot. One Eye might accept this explanation.

His more silent companion with the braces helped. "It is true that to consult the Book of Changes or the calendar for lucky and unlucky days is an excellent way to remain healthy."

As he spoke, several others of their wretched horde approached. One of them carried dominoes. "Have you cash to gamble tonight?" he asked. Quickly all were engrossed in the patter of dice, dominoes, and strings of cash.

Chu rose immediately. "Since we have nothing to gamble, we will walk a little."

The beggars neither heard nor cared, and Chu and Hsu Ta slipped away.

They slept that night on the stones near the East Gate of the city, and when the doors clanged open in the first light of morning, Chu and Hsu Ta entered Hangchow.

"Have you ever seen so many people!" gasped Hsu Ta, as they were caught up in a swarm of runners with their loads balanced on the ends of carrying poles, vendors with their wares in baskets, ladies riding in curtained litters, men of the gentry class on horses, and crowds of people scurrying about to begin their day's business.

Chu reached for Hsu Ta to pull him out of the way of a handsome red wedding chair. Hidden behind the satin curtains sat a young bride on the way to her new home. A long train of runners followed, carrying her dowry of stools and tables, silk bedding, hard, lacquered pillows, and boxes of jewels, hair ornaments, and clothing.

"We borrow your light, we borrow your light," cried the runners, clearing the way for the marriage procession.

"Pig, have you no eyes?" cried a water coolie who had been stepped on.

"You, whose ancestors for ten generations have picked garbage from the streets, out of our way!" the runner replied.

"But where do so many people come from?" said Hsu Ta.

"The Fang Chang told me there are sixty million people in our country," said Chu, "and that a million of them live in Hangchow. When the barbarians took the northern capital, many people followed the Imperial Son of Heaven to this southern capital. The Fang Chang says it is the largest and richest city in the world. The thought makes me hungry," added Chu.

"Everything makes you hungry," said Hsu Ta.

For breakfast they treated themselves, with the money they had begged the night before, to a bowl of Forest of Fragrance tea and fish cooked with plums in a tiny teashop called the Longevity-and-Compassion Palace.

After breakfast, Chu said, "I want to see all of the city now." He had seen much of country ways. It was necessary for him to learn the ways of cities also.

"Why must you memorize the whole of China?" said Hsu Ta, hastily swallowing the rest of his tea and following Chu.

Hurrying through crowded store-fronted alleys, they crossed hump-backed bridges, which spanned the city's system of canals, and came finally to the wide Imperial Way bordered by the Main Canal, which ran north and south through the rectangle of Hangchow. To the south was the Imperial Palace, the Hill of Ten Thousand Pines, and Phoenix Hill where the rich lived in their mansions, the Altar for the sacrifices to Heaven and Earth, and the

Temple of Imperial Ancestors.

Chu and Hsu Ta saw the curved, yellow-tiled roofs behind the high compound walls of the mansions of the rich. They saw the crowded, two-storied houses of the poor. They saw the sprawling rice, pig, fish, salt, and jewelry markets, and in the shops along the Imperial Way, there were ornaments in gold and silver, brocades, fans, jades, porcelains, printed books, ivories, medicines, all from parts of their own country. And carried along the trade routes from the west, especially along the Silk Road, there were Persian and Arabian wares, Russian furs, rhinoceros horn from Bengal, and those strange, foreign spectacles from Italy.

There were schools, too, from the small rooms set between shops where students shouted the texts they were memorizing, to the great imperial colleges and academies for the higher education of the sons of rich mandarin families. And there were many public baths.

The Hangchow passion for luxury and pleasure was evident everywhere. People gathered in teashops and pleasure gardens, watched shadow plays, puppets, acrobats, and actors, listened to the music of panpipes, zithers, and the guitars of the singing girls, and what was left of their time they spent in feasting and gambling games, of chess, cards, Mah-Jongg, and dice.

"Look at this," said Chu angrily, staring at a painted barge with blue sails that carried a rich merchant down the Main Canal. "People starve in the rice fields and drown their infant girl children in the marshes because there is nothing left to feed another mouth. And in this city men throw away their satin shoes after a single wearing. At least it must be said," Chu added ruefully, "that the Mongols have not much changed Hangchow."

But that the Mongols made Hangchow suffer, too, grew more apparent as the evening came. There was a curfew for the Chinese. Once they had feasted in the light of many-colored lanterns through the night. Now no Chinese could be on the streets or in public places after dark.

"How is it," asked Hsu Ta, "that a people who for a thousand years have known the art of printing, who make medicines, and instruments to study the stars, and cannon to shoot gunpowder—how is it we were conquered by these stupid barbarians?"

They both knew the answer to that, Chu reflected. He had once written an exercise for the Fang Chang on that subject.

"It is because our highest ideal is learning, and theirs is the art of war; and because, although the great emperors of the past were strong enough both to extend our boundaries and defend the Middle Kingdom against these Tartars, our government was weak two hundred years ago when Genghis Khan first rode down upon us with his Golden Hordes. He knew how to beat us, burning villages and murdering millions of our people, and then forcing the best Chinese engineers and surgeons and our men of learning into his service."

Three Mongol horsemen clattered behind them on the paving stones of the Imperial Way. Chu and Hsu Ta jumped aside.

"Will we never be done with them?" asked Hsu Ta grimly.

"Yes," said Chu, his voice calm. "When all of China unites to push them back over the Great Wall into their deserts. But as long as there are only small rebellions here and there, and the chieftains fight among themselves for power, nothing can be accomplished."

The Mongols had stopped. Two dismounted from their horses, and Chu and Hsu Ta could see that their object was an elderly man. He wore a long black silk robe and the black cap of a scholar. Chu crept closer and saw that the old man's face was ashen with terror, as the soldiers pinned him against the wall at the point of their lances. The crowd, which had begun to gather, quickly dispersed.

"Please, Honored Sirs, take my purse," wailed the old man. He untied his purse from the girdle at his waist and held it out in his long-nailed hand.

One of the soldiers laughed cruelly and emptied the purse on the ground. Out spilled a small abacus, a hand-kerchief, keys, and some paper money.

"I will count ten," said the soldier. "If by that time you have not picked up my box—" He paused to point to a large chest before one of the shops. He had obviously ordered merchandise to be ready for him.

"I would if I could," said the old scholar. "I have no strength left in this unworthy back. Will you permit me to find a young load-bearer for you?"

"If I had wanted a coolie, I could have found one for myself." Chu heard the soldier reply with a harsh laugh. "You may think the greatest power lies in the mind and the greatest wisdom is that of an old ancient like yourself. But I will show you that the greatest power lies in the sword and the greatest wisdom in those who use it best. Now—one, two, three—"

Chu, who had witnessed such cruelty all his life, could no longer listen. Infuriated by such treatment of an old scholar, by the memory of how his parents and his brother had starved, and by thoughts of his last day at the monastery, he felt a stronger hatred of the Mongols than he had ever felt before. He undid the rope that girdled his waist and slashed at the horse of the mounted soldier. The horse plunged away down the avenue. The two dismounted soldiers were too surprised ot react quickly. Chu stunned one of them from behind with a heavy blow on the back of his neck. The other he faced with his fists raised. The Mongol grinned and readied his lance.

"Take the scholar and run," Chu ordered Hsu Ta.

When the two were safely down a nearby alley, it was Chu's turn to grin. He had twice the size and strength and a hundred times the courage of the barbarian who waved the lance in front of him, and just before he died on the point of his own lance, the Mongol must have realized this. There was a look of terror on his face as he slid silently to the ground at Chu's feet.

Hsu Ta, having left the old scholar in a nearby tea garden to recover himself, hurried back.

"We must leave the city at once," he cried, "before the body is discovered or that other one wakes up. The gates will be closing, Chu, hurry."

Together they raced through the streets and across the canal bridges. For a short time they lost their way in a quarter where streets twisted in abrupt angles to keep out evil spirits which could travel only in a straight line.

"Where is the nearest gate?" Chu asked of a group of children playing in the street with their dog.

The children sang out directions, and Chu and Hsu Ta sped on. They reached a gate at the west end of the city only moments before it clanged shut. A little farther, and they found themselves on the shore of the beautiful Western Lake. It would of course be patrolled by the soldiers, but Chu and Hsu Ta had become masters at hiding from patrols.

As they crept toward a grove of bamboos on the rim of

the lake, Chu caught his breath at the loveliness of Hangchow's scenery, so famous that it had been painted by the
greatest Chinese artists and described by the greatest poets.
The yellow moon was a lantern over the misty blue-green
hills; the scene reminded him of one of the Fang Chang's
hanging scrolls painted by the Sung artist Ma Yuan. The
wooded islands and shores of the lake sheltered hundreds
of pavilions, summer houses, pagodas, and palaces. On the
horizon, like a backdrop, were mountains with deep valleys
and curiously shaped peaks. Chu saw the roofs of a Buddhist monastery clinging to the side of a distant cliff. Small
waves lapped against the sides of a nearby barge with a
dragon prow. Otherwise all except the wind in the leaves
was still. The curfew was in force.

"How gay it all must have been in the evenings during
the times of the Sung emperors," whispered Hsu Ta.

"We must turn time back," Chu stormed angrily. "We
must make it all the way it was before, in Sung times, and
in the days of Tang."

"I have heard it said," answered Hsu Ta, "that to turn
backwards is to die. Ought we not to keep some of the
things the Mongols have taught us? For instance, to keep
open the trade routes to the West?"

"We need nothing from the West," said Chu. "China is
enough in itself. No, all must be as it was before."

Chu turned to see if he had convinced Hsu Ta of this
idea, but, as if in protest, Hsu Ta had fallen asleep.

Bandits

H SU TA SLEPT well that night in the bamboo grove, but Chu did not sleep at all. Instead he sat, staring at the soaring Thunder Point Pagoda, or watching the yellow moon on the waters of the Western Lake and the mists of vapor that shrouded the mountains towards morning. As he sat, he thought of China's destiny and his own, and when the sun rose behind him over the walls of Hangchow, Chu had decided what he must do.

He woke Hsu Ta gently and spoke his thoughts.

"For two years I studied the Wu Chin, the Five Classics of Changes, of History, Poetry, Rites, and the Spring and Autumn Annals, and learned the Ssu Shu, the Four Books of Confucius. For two more years I have wandered the country and learned the ways and thoughts of people. I am nearly twenty-two, and the time has come to begin what I wish to do in my life."

51

"In the Book of Tao, Lao Tzu says, 'Do nothing and all things will be done,'" said Hsu Ta with a mocking smile. "But since you, like Confucius, are more concerned with organizing the proper life for man on earth than following the Taoist Way, which allows a man to reach Heavenly peace, tell me your plan."

"I am going to join the rebels now," said Chu, taking a deep breath.

It was not easy for Chu to say those words. His mother would not have approved, nor his father. Chu himself had been struggling against the impulse for four years, partly to acquire knowledge, and partly to honor the memory of his parents—his father who wished him to farm and his mother who wished him to become a scholar. Chu wasn't certain even in his own mind of the wisdom of his choice. Many of the rebel groups were as much interested in filling their own stomachs and pockets as in helping China. But at least they were fighting, and that was what Chu felt he must do.

"I must," added Chu, aloud.

"Would it make your heart less heavy to ask the old Fang Chang's blessing?" asked Hsu Ta.

"That's what I was thinking," said Chu. "I'll go back now to Hua Shan. Then I will search for Liu Fu-t'ung."

Liu was a name spoken with fear and awe along the lower Yangtze River. His increasing band of rebels lived, hid, and fought Mongol garrisons in the marshes and along the lakes, rivers, and canal systems of the eastern Yangtze region. It was rumored that although his headquarters were at Lake Po-yang, at present he was not far from the Hua Shan monastery in Chu's own province of Anhui. Liu's men were said to be the fiercest and best trained guerrilla fighters of all. They were called the Red Turbans from the color of the kerchief they tied about their heads. Their numbers had grown, some said, to nearly one hundred thousand men.

Chu stood up, and Hsu Ta rose, too.

"Walk carefully," said Chu, meaning goodbye. "You will be safe here behind the high walls of Hangchow."

"I had the feeling you meant to leave me here," said Hsu Ta. "Shall I then apprentice myself to a guild or open a small shop or grow fat and rich working for the white-skinned Big Noses while you do my fighting for me? Besides, how will you buy morning rice, since I am the only one with money. The old scholar gave me this which he had hidden in his sleeve after we saved his life yesterday." From his own sleeve, Hsu Ta took out a string of five hundred copper cash. It would buy food for many days.

"You have a stubborn heart," said Chu, though he knew it wasn't stubborness but devotion that made Hsu Ta refuse the safety of life in Hangchow to follow him back to Anhui.

They bought breakfast from one of the floating barge restaurants on the Western Lake and began their journey north. As the day went by, they passed villages and walled towns and crossed the irrigation ditches between rice fields set like emeralds among the spring-blooming mustard flowers. It was not long before they left the province of Chekiang to enter the rich region of southern Anhui below the Yangtze River. Eventually they climbed the foothills of Anhui's mountains, and then the mountains themselves, the steep gorges and jagged rocky cliffs where nets of mist drifted and waterfalls plunged into chasms. Now and then they saw a temple among the tall pines in the cleft of a mountain, or the half-hidden hut of a hermit by a thin, silver stream. But these were the only reminders of the world of men. For the rest, the mountains were empty and silent.

Chu and Hsu Ta approached the Hua Shan mountain early in summer. Chu had very nearly decided to search for the rebels without pausing to visit the Fang Chang, so impatient was he to raise his sword against the Mongols. But in the nearby villages, he heard whispered conversations of terrible happenings at Hua Shan, and changed his mind.

As they climbed toward the monastery, the mountain silence was suddenly broken by loud cries, uttered and then echoed again by the valley walls. Chu lifted his head and detected the sharp smell of smoke.

"There!" cried Chu, pointing upward. An orange lick of flame blazed suddenly against the sky. "Did you see it?"

"Is it the monastery?" asked Hsu Ta.

"It must be. Hurry," said Chu, his heart thickening with fear for the old Fang Chang, as he rushed up the mountainside.

Hsu Ta scrambled after Chu. "Don't you think it would be wiser to go to the village first and find out what's happened?" said Hsu Ta.

But Chu heard only the echoing cries and raced on. As he broke through the edge of the pines, he saw that the broad clearing in front of the monastery walls was filled with hundreds of monks. Their cries were deafening, and Chu felt their panic run like a tremor through his own body. Some were making bundles out of the few possessions they had managed to rescue. Several devout *lohans* were on their knees, touching their prayer beads and chanting prayers from the Lotus Sutra. One monk, his gray robe scorched brown, ran madly around in circles, wailing for the protection of Buddha, his ancestors, the Dragon Kings, and the Jade Emperor of Heaven all at once. The wounded, untended, lay helpless beneath the trees.

"I see no Mongols," said Chu, grabbing the sleeve of a monk's robe to question him.

The monk blinked at Chu and babbled in his terror. "The Mongols have gone."

"That doesn't make sense," Chu shouted above the noise. "Why should they take the monastery and then leave? It's too excellent a stronghold to desert."

"They didn't desert it," the monk shouted back. "There was a battle, and they were burned out. So were we. Now what is to become of us?"

"But who did this? Who attacked the monastery?" persisted Chu.

"About two years ago, a troop of Mongols came."

"I remember that," said Chu. "It was then that I had to leave Hua Shan."

The monk nodded, but didn't look as if he remembered the small incident. "Afterwards, the Mongols garrisoned many soldiers here."

"But why did they burn the monastery?" Chu asked again as the monk lapsed once more into silence.

"It wasn't the Mongols who started the fire. It was the bandits. A large band of rebels attacked the Mongols of Hua Shan last night. They killed the Mongols, but during the battle, the monastery caught fire."

"Where are the bandits now?" asked Chu.

The monk pointed in the direction of the monastery walls. "In there," he said, his voice rising in terror.

"Go and sit down under the trees now," said Chu gently. "Everything will be all right."

But before he let the monk's sleeve go, Chu asked one more question.

"The Fang Chang, where is he?"

The monk shook his head. "I don't know."

Chu stared about him. The confusion was growing worse. As more monks spilled out of the monastery gates, they jostled and trampled on each other for space. Chu took a deep breath. He had never given orders before, but clearly something had to be done before the crowd either stampeded or, if the wind changed direction, got caught in the spreading fire. Chu glanced up over the wall at the great curves of the tiled roofs. As yet the front halls were untouched, but from beyond smoke and flame rose in angry, bellowing leaps. There wasn't much time. He began to give orders rapidly, using the same words over and over again as he pushed through the crowds.

"Go quietly and quickly down the mountain. Go south, to the monastery on the island of P'u T'o where you will be safe. P'u T'o is sacred to Kuan Yin, the Goddess of Mercy. She will keep you safe." Over and over, Chu chanted these words like a litany. When he saw someone who was wounded, he said, "Go and lie under the trees. I will send a doctor."

Whether it was the sight of the huge stranger in the tattered sky-blue coat, or the gentle concern in his face, or simply the calm authority of his voice, the general panic lessened, and the monks began to organize themselves for flight.

"He is too young to give orders to his elders," grumbled someone.

"Be still. He speaks the only wisdom I have heard today," someone else replied. "He is right. We must go to the monastery on the island of P'u T'o, and we must do so without trampling each other to death."

"Where are your doctors?" asked Chu, picking up a

monk with a head wound and carrying him to the edge of the clearing.

"Behind the walls. The rebels keep those with knowledge and skills for their own service."

"Then be patient. I will see that a doctor is sent out," said Chu.

"You're going inside there?" asked the wounded monk. "You must be crazy. Bandits are as ruthless as Mongols. They will kill you if you interfere with them."

"They won't kill me," said Chu with a smile. "From this day on, I am one of them."

As he placed the wounded monk on a soft bed of pine needles, Chu caught sight of Hsu Ta who, following Chu's example, moved among the jostling monks to calm them and urge them to begin their journey.

"Stay with the wounded," said Chu, beckoning to Hsu Ta.

Hsu Ta nodded, and Chu increased his effort to clear the grounds. Soon the monks began to stream through the forest and down the mountain, still frightened but at least moving. In half an hour, the last of the monks had fled, and the injured were made comfortable under Hsu Ta's care.

Chu faced the burning monastery he was about to enter. He thought how years before he would have been frightened of the Fire Dragon's wrath. He had just helped to save many people from the fire spirit, and this, Chu's father would have said, was enough to cause the Dragon's undying anger. But if he had learned nothing else in the years since he had left Chung-li, he had at least overcome his superstitions.

If facing the fire held no fear for Chu, facing the bandits was another matter. Before he joined them openly, he wanted to find the Fang Chang and get him safely away from the monastery. If the bandits caught Chu doing this, they might easily misunderstand him. Bandits were known to trust no one who had ideas of his own.

Quietly Chu crept through the partly open gate. The wide entry court was deserted, but lest it be watched, Chu used the covered corridor at the side of the rectangular court to reach the Hall of the Four Heavenly Kings. All was still and dim under the vast carved rafters, and for a moment Chu rested against a wooden pillar. From there he could hear the commotion in the court of the Great Main Hall. Chu moved closer to the rear verandah, and peered through the latticework of the temple door.

"The roof! The roof is burning," Chu heard someone shout. He looked up and saw a burning ember among the blue tiles on the overhanging eave of the Great Main Hall.

"Who will climb up to the roof and knock off that piece of wood?" shouted a voice whose tones Chu recognized. Brother Wang! But why was he in a position to give orders?

It was a question Chu decided he would deal with later. Now there was no time. He must find the Fang Chang. It was some relief, however, to know that the bandits did not intend to burn the entire monastery to the ground.

Chu left the Hall of the Four Heavenly Kings by a side door, and moving through a maze of corridors and courts and outbuildings managed eventually to reach the Fang Chang's pavilion, at least what was left of it. Most of the pavilion had been burned. Only the rear walls and part of the side still stood, supporting a fragment of roof. On this fragment of roof, strangely untouched, the Feng-huang, the gilded sacred Phoenix of good fortune, shone in the golden rays of the setting sun.

Maddened that the symbol should survive but not his

old friend, Chu flung himself into the charred remains of the pavilion and began, with his powerful arms, to thrust aside fallen pillars and rafters and to claw at the piles of rubble. He was so possessed with rage at yet another death of one close to him, that he did not realize he was crying.

Even when he was seized from behind, Chu could not stop clawing at the remains of the Fang Chang's pavilion. Flinging off the two men who tried to seize him, Chu continued his search. Then four others came and then six more, and they bound his wrists and feet, slung him on a carrying pole like a great tiger brought down from the mountain, and bore him off to the Great Main Hall. There, on a chair placed under the statue of the Lord of Hell, sat the Captain of the rebel band who had taken Hua Shan. Chu was thrown at his feet.

"Kill him." The cold, cruel voice was that of Brother Wang, standing near the right hand of the rebel Captain. A malicious smile creased the thickly fleshed face, and the nine sacred scars on his head gleamed dully in the dimly lit Hall. By what right, Chu wondered, did Brother Wang advise the Captain?

"Kill him," Brother Wang repeated. "This man was searching for the Fang Chang. He is a Mongol spy."

Red Turbans

W HY SHOULD that make him a spy?" the Captain asked.

Brother Wang's voice was smooth, oily, persuasive.

"If the Mongols have the Fang Chang, who is sacred to the people of this region, they can use him to bend the people to their will. Clearly they sent this man to capture the Fang Chang for them and to spy on our movements while he was at it."

"Nonsense!"

Chu's voice rang out so clearly and so rudely that it caused a shocked silence among the assembled rebels. Two or three came forward to kick him into silence, but the Captain raised his hand.

"When one's hands and feet are bound, and one lies helpless at the feet of an enemy, such impoliteness is the mark either of a fool or a man of great courage. I would like to determine which, before putting him to death," said the Captain. He bent forward to examine Chu, his black eyes glinting with humor. "Now, Insignificance, speak and tell me who you are and why you were looking for the Fang Chang."

"I searched for the Fang Chang because he is my old and dear friend, the Master who taught me for two years here at Hua Shan. This, Brother Wang knows perfectly well, as he knows me perfectly well. He lies about me. Why do you listen to him?"

"I listen to him because he is a powerful member of the White Lotus sect, whose armed monks have been our allies against the Mongols for some time. There, I have explained my position, unworthy dog. I am still waiting for you to explain yours." The Captain's voice was not unkind, and his round, unwashed face remained cheerful.

"My mission is simple," explained Chu. "I wish to join the Red Turbans under General Liu. I came here only to ask the Fang Chang's blessing first."

"He lies," said Brother Wang coldly.

"Be quiet," said the Captain cheerfully.

Brother Wang bowed and was silent. It was acknowledgement that despite his dirty cheerfulness, the rebel leader had the greater power.

"Look around you," the Captain said to Chu. "What do you see?"

Chu managed to sit up, in spite of his still bound hands and feet, and look around. He saw torn jackets and trousers, unkempt hair and half-grown beards, dirty sandals and unwashed faces. But in the face of each man, he saw proud, bright eyes and on each head, like a defiant banner, a red scarf tied around the brow.

"Red Turbans," cried Chu. "Am I so fortunate as to be

in the presence of General Liu?"

"Not quite so fortunate," answered the Captain with a grin, "but almost. I am Kuo Tsu-hsing, Captain under General Liu." He paused and leaned forward again. "And now will you please, for the last time, tell me who *you* are."

"Your nephew, Chu Yuan-chang," said Chu promptly, and answered Kuo's grin with his own.

Kuo frowned, as if Chu had made a joke in bad taste. Or as if, by mentioning the relationship, Chu had put Kuo under an obligation Kuo did not wish to honor.

"Take him away," said Kuo abruptly. "Put him with the other one."

Startled by the sudden change of attitude, but obedient, several men hoisted Chu back onto the pole and carried him off. As Chu was taken away, he heard Brother Wang's voice.

"That is what the pig deserves."

Chu raged at Brother Wang's emphasis on the word *pig*. It was a homophone for his own name. Although the characters were written differently with the brush, the word for pig spoken aloud was the same sound as Chu. Someday, he would repay the power-hungry Brother Wang for every insult, as bitter to taste as torture.

When they had thrust Chu into a small, dark cell, the men unbound his hands and feet. Crawling around in the darkness, he soon found the other occupant of the cell. It was the Fang Chang.

"I have no strength to waste in being surprised to find you here," said the Fang Chang, speaking in his usual dry voice but with difficulty. "Soon I will Ascend the Dragon." His manners were perfect still, and good taste forbade him to use the word for death.

"Don't go," whispered Chu, slipping his strong arm under the thin, frail shoulders of his master.

The Fang Chang shook his head impatiently for silence. "I have no wish to live through these troubled times. I can see now that revolution is inevitable. Since the death of Kublai Khan fifty years ago, the Mongol emperors have grown weak and cruel; and throughout our history, the Chinese people have used their right to take back the Mandate of Heaven from unjust rulers."

The Fang Chang paused for breath before going on. "I know why you came back, my young friend. It was to ask my blessing as you join the rebels."

Chu said darkly, " 'The emperor is like a boat, the people are like water. Water will support the boat, but it can also submerge it.' "

"Yes, yes. And 'The safety of the Jade Palace can only be guaranteed by a bowl of rice in the mud hut.' But please, no more old Chinese sayings, O Fountain of Wisdom," the Fang Chang begged, with a return of his old humor. "I want only to ask this of you: that when the fighting is over, you will help to bring peace to this country and a return to the ancient ways, so that once again, China will be a civilized land of harmonious relationships and the moral virtues preached by the sages. And one thing more."

The Fang Chang struggled to sit up a little to make his last request.

"I have no sons to honor me after my soul has departed."

"Be peaceful, adoptive father," said Chu. "When I have a home, I will set your soul tablet next to those of my parents and burn incense and paper spirit money in your honor as in theirs."

"Ten thousand thanks," murmured the Fang Chang, and drew his last breath peacefully in Chu's arms.

"Don't die," whispered Chu, his eyes open and burning in the darkness. He could not cry. The sorrow in him, for the Fang Chang, for his starved family, for his cruelly tortured country, had hardened into an anger that twisted sharp as a sword in the heart. Chu waited only for the time when the gods would permit him to wrench the sword from his own heart and plunge it into the bellies of the enemy.

How long he sat there, he didn't know. He hadn't moved when Kuo burst into the cell with a lighted torch.

Fat and dirty, the Captain squatted on his heels next to Chu and greeted him cheerfully.

"Forgive me for treating you like this," said Kuo.

"What is next?" asked Chu in bitterness. "Will you hang the wooden collar around my neck and send me to the frontiers? Or sentence me to the death of a thousand cuts? Or just hang me up in a wire cage until I starve to death?"

"Maybe I will have you beaten with the heavy bamboo whip, but only if you won't be quiet and listen to me," Kuo said, laughing. "First, I had you brought in here so that you might see the Ancient One before he died. He defied me for many months when I asked for his help in defeating the Mongols, and I would have lost face if I had had him brought out to you. And then there was Brother Wang's face to save. He was so anxious to have you killed. I couldn't hurt his feelings, since the White Lotus monks have been most helpful to us. But Brother Wang is gone now, so you needn't remain in this cell any longer. I will have the Fang Chang buried with honor on a lucky day and according to the good and evil forces of *feng shui*, in a lucky site. In the meantime, I invite you to have dinner with me and meet my officers."

"I have a request," said Chu woodenly.

"Make it."

"My friend Hsu Ta waits outside the walls with the wounded monks. Will you send a surgeon and food?"

"The matter has been attended to already," said Kuo. "The wounded have been brought inside the walls and your friend Hsu Ta is sleeping comfortably this minute."

"Thank you," said Chu simply.

"And for yourself, no doubt you would like a bath. My sister was always uncommonly clean," said Kuo.

After a bath in water warmed with a hot stone, Chu was given the short coat, trousers, and boots of a soldier, and when he entered the dining room he found, next to his rice bowl, the red scarf that marked the rebel band. He had only to wind it around his forehead to signify his member-ship in the Red Turbans.

From their places at the tables, the whole band watched as Chu bowed three times to Kuo, placed the scarf on his head, and took the seat Kuo offered at his right. All cheered loudly and lifted their cups of rice wine. Hsu Ta, also in soldier's boots and red scarf, cheered along with them.

"Nothing is too good for the son of my elder sister, eh?" said Kuo, gesturing toward the bowls of food on the table. There were, besides the rice, dishes of shredded pork and chicken cooked with leeks, goose cooked with apricots, lotus seed soup, and pimento soup with mussels, dishes of noodles and bean curd, water chestnuts, and sugar bean cakes; and in addition to rice wine, there were honey and ginger drinks and dark, green tea.

"A feast for mandarins, yes?" said Kuo, beaming.

"I am not worthy," Chu murmured politely. But he was ravenously hungry and ate well.

While Chu rested between courses, Kuo refilled Chu's wine cup. "Tell me now of my elder sister."

When Chu had spoken of the last terrible year on the farm, of the death of his parents and brother, Kuo heaved a large sigh. It sounded to Chu like a sigh of relief.

"At least the bandits did not raid my elder sister's home?" he asked.

"No. They raided neighboring farms and the village. We wondered why they left us alone," answered Chu.

"My orders," said Kuo simply. Those simple words impressed Chu more than any display of force could have done.

"Men fear you then, Uncle Kuo?"

"I left Nanking where your mother and I were born before your mother married into the Chu family. I went to Ting-yuan in the province of Shensi and began a business as a wine merchant. There I quarreled with a man who dealt unfairly with me, lost my temper, and accidentally killed him. Since the man was a Mongol official, I lost no time in escaping to join the rebel forces. You can see for yourself," Kuo finished with a broad wink, "that a violent temper runs in our family."

"And your wife and children?" Chu asked politely.

"I have managed to return them to Nanking," said Kuo. "My wife, my son, and my daughter live again in the House of Kuo. As a matter of fact, I must go there next week to meet with General Liu. I insist that you be my guest."

Chu bowed in gratitude for his uncle's patronage, but there was no time for his uncle to return the bow. A handsome young man came hurriedly into the dining hall and immediately to Kuo.

"I've just received news that Chang is making trouble again up the Yangtze River near Lake Po-yang."

"Sit down, sit down, and eat something," Kuo boomed cheerfully to the young man. "I want you to meet my nephew, Chu Yuan-chang. He has just become one of us." Kuo turned to Chu. "And this is Han Lin-erh, my most important Lieutenant. He worries a great deal."

"There is a great deal to worry over," said Han, pulling up an extra chair. Yet despite his worry, his voice was calm, the sign to Chu of a controlled disposition.

"He speaks of Chang and other leaders of rebel bands like Chang, who live in the marshes along the Yangtze and fight among themselves instead of fighting Mongols," Kuo explained. "Chang is the strongest, so Han worries about him most."

"They must be united," said Chu abruptly. "And they must stop pillaging and starving the farmers by their plunder."

"Only ten minutes ago he put on his red scarf, and already he begins to organize the rebellion," Kuo remarked slowly. His tone remained light enough, but Chu sensed the undercurrent of warning common to overbearing men who did not want their authority threatened in any way. Chu would have argued further, but he was beginning to understand the differences in the temperaments of men, and he decided quickly that this was no time to press the matter.

"I wish only to see the Red Turbans take the lead over all other bands. And if others plunder, what will be left to feed our army when it breaks out openly against the Mongols?" said Chu persuasively.

"What do you mean, breaks out openly against the Mongols? We must fight in secret, or face the wrath of imperial troops," said Kuo, but he was appeased by Chu's loyalty to himself and the Red Turbans, and again raised his cup of wine to continue the feasting and drinking.

But if Chu's remarks only glanced off Kuo's vanity, they seemed to make a deep impression on Han.

"The gods bring us good fortune in your nephew, Captain Kuo," Han said in his cool voice. "We have great need of leaders—under your direction, of course—" Han put in with a bow to Kuo, "to put an end to the confusion among the rebels and the plundering of innocent people." Savoring his wine, Han stared at Chu over the rim of his cup.

Chu wondered what Han was thinking as he stared. He did not find out, for Han was a man who obviously did not betray his thoughts easily. Yet, raising his wine cup in a gesture so slight that only Chu saw it, Han toasted Chu, and Chu, with the smallest nod of his head, accepted Han's gesture as friendship.

Jade and Peonies

OVER A THOUSAND years before, under the
King of Wu, and then under the southern imperial
dynasties of Chin and Ch'i, Nanking, near the mouth of
the Yangtze River, had once been a great capital. It was
still a center of wealth, and if weeds grew now in the
imperial courts, the merchants and ruling mandarin class
prospered.

Though not the most ancient, in the past few years the
House of Kuo had become one of the largest and richest,
not only in the city of Nanking, but throughout the district and even the whole province of Kiangsu. This was
due entirely to the efforts of Kuo himself, whose business
ability was, if anything, superior to his military ability.
Some said his fortune now amounted to tens of thousands
of strings of cash, some said hundreds of thousands. It was
true that Kuo gave a great deal of his money to the rebel
cause, but Chu could see that Kuo also kept a great deal
for himself. It was a tribute to the failing and corrupt
Mongol regime, and to the cleverness with which Kuo
chose his business managers, that Kuo's fortune had been
amassed and he himself had been able to live in Nanking

above suspicion. It had also to be said that Kuo knew whom and when to bribe among the officials.

With Hsu Ta and Han, Chu entered Nanking at Kuo's side. Since Kuo's identity in the city was established as a rich merchant who carried on a prosperous trade in drugs and surgical supplies, he had dressed them each in the suitably dignified clothes of fellow merchants. Chu wore a green brocaded robe with wide sleeves, silk stockings, and black satin shoes and cap. Around his waist, the girdle was clasped with a buckle of carved jade. Never had he worn clothes like these, and he moved carefully so as not to soil anything. At the edge of the city, Kuo sent the horses, forbidden to Chinese, back with his men, and hired carrying-chairs to bring them to the gates of his house.

"So many gates," said Chu, praising Kuo's wealth politely.

The high wall that surrounded Kuo's mansion and estate was indeed impressive. Two huge stone lions guarded the two smaller gates, and over the main gate there was a panel bearing the characters *ning kuo fu* meaning "peace to the country mansion." A dozen manservants and maids came to greet them and escort them through the entry court and under a second gate hung with flowers. In this court there was a fragrant lotus pool, and beyond was the Main Hall with carved beams and red lacquered pillars.

Chu felt he had entered a world of dreams. Never had he imagined the existence of anything so lovely. With Han and Hsu Ta in their wake, Kuo showed Chu the whole of his home. Beautifully furnished rooms encircled court after court. Sometimes one court was set directly behind another and could be entered through a round moon gate. Other courts were set at angles and connected by covered corridors.

When Chu had seen the mansion, Kuo showed him the

parks beyond. Paths led among groves of peach trees and bamboo and mulberry trees for the silkworms. In the center of a small lake was an artificial mountain with a summerhouse, which could be reached by crossing a marble bridge or in a tiny boat moored to the lake's edge. Pleasure pavilions were half-hidden among the trees and shrubs, and near a winding stream were exquisitely shaped rocks, dwarfed pines, and gardens of peonies and orchids.

A peal of silvery laughter floated through the warm, summer afternoon. Chu thought it came from an enclosed court to his left.

Kuo nodded in that direction and grinned at Chu. "Those are the Red Chambers, the rooms where the unmarried ladies of the household live, under the supervision of my daughter Ma Hou. And that laugh could only belong to her maid Apricot. Now," said Kuo, turning to go back into the house, "come to the Main Hall where Madame Kuo and my son will be waiting to give us tea."

Passing through the Main Hall with its polished floor, its elegant red and black lacquer tables and chairs, and a landscape scroll that covered the whole of one wall, they went out onto the moon-viewing verandah where Kuo's wife and son had ordered the tea things to be brought.

"*Tai-tai,*" murmured Han in greeting to the First Mistress of the house. He had visited often, and Chu noticed that Kuo's wife took pleasure in welcoming him again.

"Our sister's youngest son, and his friend Hsu Ta," said Kuo, presenting Chu to Madame Kuo and to Young Kuo, a small, muscular boy still in his teens who looked as if he would grow up to resemble his father exactly.

"And General Liu, when will he come?" asked Chu, after the usual polite greetings had been exchanged.

"Hush," cautioned Han. "In Nanking even the walls, but most especially the servants, have ears. Here we simply call him Lord Liu."

"Our young relative, who has not yet so much as led his first raid, is most anxious to begin the reorganization of our followers," Kuo whispered to his wife, his eyes bright with humor. Now that he was assured of Chu's loyalty, he seemed to accept Chu's impatience to break into open rebellion against the Mongols with a combination of family pride and good-natured indulgence.

Chu looked at Han, who had begun chatting with Madame Kuo, and Kuo, noticing, said, "Han is the son of my friend from the Northern Capital of Peking—I can not call it Cambaluc, after the manner of the Mongols. Han's father was executed for his connection with the White Lotus sect. Afterwards, Han escaped to Anhui and found Liu's fighting forces under my command. He has become a favorite of Liu, and I have made him an adoptive son. I have it in mind one day to give Han my daughter Ma Hou in marriage. He has a brilliant administrative mind," added Kuo.

Chu stored the information about Han in his mind. It was always good to learn what one could about men's lives.

The tea conversation went on as Chu sat back and took in the grandeur of his uncle's home. Comfortable as it was, he hoped they would not stay too long. He would get soft. And that would do nothing for China. Yet Han did not seem worried. Still, he was different, more a man of planning, Chu had already decided, than a man of firm action.

After tea, Chu and Hsu Ta were shown to their rooms in the western wing of the house. Bath water was brought for the tub, and fresh inner and outer robes had been laid out for them. They were told by one of the maids that a feast was being prepared, but it would not be held until late in the night, and in the meantime they were to rest and refresh themselves.

"I know you better than to imagine you are tired," said Hsu Ta when he had attended to Chu's bath as he always did, insisting on waiting on Chu himself. "But if you don't need me, do you mind if I sleep for an hour or two?"

"You are half asleep now," said Chu. "You might just as well make the rest of the journey. I will dress and walk in the courtyard for a while."

As he paced slowly in the court, Chu heard the sound of silvery laughter. It was the same sound he had heard during the afternoon, and feeling lonely, he followed the sound until he came to the court of the Red Chambers. Although he knew it was forbidden to enter the courts of unmarried women, he could not resist at least a brief glance.

The scene was breathtakingly lovely, as he paused for a moment in the shadow of the moon gate. A yellow moon shone in the dusky blue sky and under the eaves of the dim room beyond, the glow of yellow lamplight shone in

the latticework window. Through the half-open door, surrounded by her attendants, sat a young girl. Slender as a
willow in her long-sleeved jacket and trousers, her black
hair curled and piled thickly with gold ornaments on her
head, she was the most enchanting creature Chu had ever
seen. He could not leave off staring at her pale round face,
at her clear, almond-shaped eyes under brows curved like
the crescent of the moon.

Without thinking, Chu moved closer, coming at last to
lean against the carved railing of her verandah. Under the
pale yellow silk of her trousers, he saw her tiny satin-slip-
pered feet, bound as his mother's had been, after the
fashion of the tenth century Empress, who had been the
first to wrap her feet tightly in bandages and call the
crippled results Golden Lilies. Because the early months of
footbinding hurt terribly and afterwards walking was difficult, in the farmlands of Anhui where everyone was
needed to work in the fields, women did not bind their
daughters' feet. But Chu's mother had told him that fashionable city women agreed it was better to stand the agony
of footbinding and to please men with small feet than to
bear the shame of large feet.

As he stood there marveling at her, thinking he was still
unseen, her clear voice broke through his thoughts.

"You mustn't stand there like that. You are either to
come in or go away."

"You will frighten him off with that bold tone," said an
old nurse crossly. "Which is just as well. Unmarried ladies
ought not to receive gentlemen in their courts."

Chu was startled by the word gentleman. He supposed
it must be his purple silk robe and the jewels in his cap.

A peal of bright laughter, which Chu supposed must
belong to the maid Apricot, interrupted the old nurse's
scolding. "You mustn't talk to our *Nai-nai,* the Second

Mistress, like that. You know the Master permits her to do as she pleases."

As the ladies were arguing, Chu climbed the stairs to the verandah and came to stand in the open doorway of the room.

"Only small men mind boldness in a woman," said Chu, smiling. "And as you can see, I am anything but small."

A flush crept into her cheeks and her eyes grew suddenly bright. Her soft quick breathing seemed to mingle with the scent of the peonies from the court, and as Chu gazed down on her, he felt as if he were holding a blossom that must belong to him forever.

Apricot pushed forward a chair for him to sit on.

"He mustn't stay here," the old nurse scolded, whispering to Apricot. "Can't you see what is happening between them?"

"Even if I had no eyes, 'by the pervading fragrance of the flowers, one knows that the day is warm.' " Apricot merrily quoted the line from an old poem.

Chu remained silent, simply looking.

"It's true you must go," Ma Hou said finally. "My father wishes to announce my betrothal to Han Lin-erh."

Chu's face darkened, as he remembered that Kuo had indeed mentioned this to him. "Have the betrothal presents been exchanged?" he asked.

"Not yet," Ma Hou said softly.

"Then do not count on leaving this court until I return for you," said Chu abruptly. Chu laughed as the ladies gasped at his boldness. He knew such matters were family affairs, arranged properly with a pair of go-betweens in veils and purple jackets. Most certainly such decisions were never left to the young. It was true, he had heard, that Ma Hou had been educated and brought up by her father with nearly as much freedom as a son, but to suggest that her marriage would not be handled in the proper way was an unheard of breach in propriety. Besides, Chu knew Han was the handsomer and his upbringing civilized, while he himself would be regarded as an upstart from the country. Yet when Chu glanced at Ma Hou, it was evident that she did not mind his boldness a bit.

She sat in silence for a moment, her clear eyes returning Chu's steady gaze. Her slender fingers trailed across a rose jade amulet, which hung about her neck on a silken cord. Spells and incantations infused into the jade by a hermit well known for his powers had made it a protective talisman. Ma Hou took the amulet from her neck and held it out to Chu.

"Wear this and go safely," she whispered, and then, in a voice that sounded to Chu like the ringing of golden bells, she added, "Come back to me soon."

As Chu took the amulet, their hands touched and he trembled.

In the distance he heard footsteps and the sound of voices calling his name. It was evidently time for the festivities, and he dared stay no longer. He left, carrying with him the piece of jade and the scent of the peonies.

The feast was already under way around the tables set up in the Main Hall. Surrounded by the clatter of dishes and household servants, Kuo's many friends and relatives, men and women at separate tables, were obviously enjoying themselves immensely. After the banquet, there was to be an historical play, and the actors were already setting up their scenery and the orchestra in the Pear Fragrance Court. Even later, there would be outings in dragon-boats on Persimmon Lake to the north of the park.

Kuo came to greet Chu himself, and after giving Hsu Ta a place at one of the tables with the young men, he conducted Chủ to a side chamber where a more private table had been arranged.

"Lord Liu is here," Kuo whispered under his breath.

Liu sat beneath a painting of the Six Sages in a Bamboo Grove, in the high place of honor, a pale, thin man in an ordinary robe of gray silk. His face was as expressionless as his robe, but the long narrow eyes were extraordinary in the peculiar penetration of their glance. Chu felt that at the instant of introduction, Liu knew everything about him there was to know. When he spoke, his voice was slow and deliberate, as if there were nothing that need be hurried under the sun.

It was a patience that must come from long years of classical education. Chu knew that Lord Liu had not only passed the provincial examinations to attain the first and second degrees of *hsiu ts'ai* and *chu jen,* but that he had taken the examinations at Peking and been awarded the highest degree of *chin shih* as well. Under a Chinese Emperor, he would have been given high honors, salaries, and an excellent official position. As matters stood, he had turned warlord instead.

On Lord Liu's right sat Kuo, and across the table from them, Chu took his place next to Han. A servant brought food and left, closing the door curtain behind him.

"I have accepted Kuo's belief in your ability and hereby make you a lieutenant under his command," Liu began slowly, indicating with a wave of his hand that he did not wish to be interrupted by Chu's thanks. "I hope that you will prove as able an officer as Han. I understand that you have ideas of your own about organizing the rebellion, that you wish to unite many troops into a single band, that you wish to order a stop to the plundering, and that, finally, you wish to attack in the open. Am I correct?"

Chu realized instantly that such an open confrontation

on Liu's part was a test. Politeness demanded that he back down before the judgment of his elders, and yet he sensed that Liu held dishonesty in contempt. In any case, there was no choice. Chu felt too strongly about the matter to hedge it about with polite embellishments.

"The Mongols do not have many garrisons in the south of China, but those they have are well fortified. An occasional attack followed by a retreat, while our bands quarrel among each other, does no good. Only an organized rebel army can wipe them out once and for all. As to the plundering of farms, I have objections not only on merciful grounds but on practical grounds as well. If we stop stealing from the farmers, they will regard us as liberators and join our cause against the Mongols. Not only will they give us freely what we do not steal, but they will march behind us when we are ready to move against the Mongols in the north. As for my feeling that we must attack openly, it is that an open rebellion will make the Mongols more afraid, and we will then have fear as an ally as well." Chu stopped, not because he felt he had been speaking too long, but because he had said all he had to say.

"Do not be angry with the boy," interrupted Kuo hastily. "His greatest passion is the destiny of China, and he sometimes oversteps—"

"I agree with Chu Yuan-chang," Lord Liu interrupted Kuo calmly. "In all but the last. I do not think the time is ripe for open rebellion. To strike fear in the heart of an enemy sometimes makes him fight all the harder for his life."

"It also makes him confused and therefore less able to fight well," said Chu.

"We will not argue the matter," said Liu. He turned to the food before him and ate it sparingly, drinking now and then iced wine from a silver cup. The others waited in silence for him to continue.

"I have another question," Liu began again. "If we succeed in winning China back from the Mongol Emperor, what reforms would you see made?" Liu's eyes looked levelly into Chu's.

Again Chu understood, that this was no time for polite evasions and false humility. And again, having pondered such questions long and hard, he felt strongly about them.

"The first is to make certain that in all eighteen provinces of China, not a single Chinese official who worked for the Mongols remains in office. There must be not only a new Emperor, but a new Grand Council, new Ministers of State, a new Board of Censors, and in each province a new Governor, in each prefecture and subprefecture, new Prefects and Magistrates. To make certain such appointments are fairly awarded, instead of merely bought by the rich and influential, we must reorganize the public schools and the system of examinations, so that all have a chance to earn the three imperial degrees."

"Agreed," murmured Liu. "What else?"

"The land taken from the Mongols and corrupt office holders must be redistributed to the peasants. Taxes must be regulated, public roads and canals repaired, coinage fixed again on a proper basis, just law for all reestablished, and the Academies of Painting and Literature restored at court."

"And what of the Japanese, whose pirates now raid our coastline?"

The Fang Chang had told Chu of the Japanese islands, which lay to the northeast across the sea. In Tang times, over five hundred years before, the Japanese had adopted and remolded for themselves much of the culture of the Middle Kingdom. They had studied the Chinese government, language, literature, arts, and sciences. They had read the Confucian Classics and Buddhist sutras, and learned iron smelting and silk and porcelain manufacture. But Japan was dominated, not by scholars, but by warrior nobles, and Chu was aware of their power.

"They were strong enough to repel the Mongols of Kublai Khan," said Chu, "and may one day be strong enough to sail the narrow Sea of Japan, cross the Korean peninsula, and invade China. We will strengthen the Great Wall and build forts along the seacoast to back up our warjunks against them."

Once, Chu thought, he could not have spoken so openly with a man as great and powerful as General Liu. But the suffering of China was so urgent in him, he felt he could have faced the Four Kings of Heaven if necessary.

"A further question," said Liu. "Would you remodel the government in any new way or continue, as the Mongols do, to learn from the scientific progress of the West?"

Chu stiffened and gazed sharply at Lord Liu. "We can do no better than to go back to our own ways. Government must be reestablished according to the manner of the glorious Tang dynasty and our schools and examinations must stress the traditional teachings of Confucius. I do not say we shouldn't trade with the Western barbarians, but we have nothing to learn from them. In China we have everything we need."

For the first time, Han's soft voice interrupted the conversation.

"It is true that in many things such as medicine and printing and firearms our technology is superior to theirs. But we have learned to make instruments to study the stars from the Moslems, and we have imported reading glasses from Italy. Would it not be better to follow the progress of the West and learn what we can?"

"Our technology is advanced enough for our purposes,"

said Chu, frowning. "And even if it could be improved, it does not seem to me that scientific progress is the way to universal harmony. No. The old ways are best. China needs stability, not change."

Han would not argue further. Instead, he fingered the soft silk of his red robe and examined the flowers and butterflies embroidered on his sleeves.

"Perhaps then we ought to keep the gates open to the West so they may learn something from us," Han said with a smile.

Chu laughed, taking pleasure in Han's cleverness. "That much I don't deny. But my concern is China, not the welfare of the Big Noses in the West."

As he looked at the handsome, charmingly dressed young man, Chu suddenly thought of Ma Hou. It seemed a miracle that she could prefer him to Han. Chu wondered what Han's feelings were, whether he loved her or had simply agreed to a family arrangement.

As he thought of Ma Hou, however, Chu felt Liu's penetrating glance and drew his thoughts back to the subject at hand. The fate of China was higher in importance than his own.

"I must think about what you have said tonight," said Liu. "At future meetings we must talk—"

A sudden commotion cut short Liu's words. Young Kuo burst through the door curtain into the small chamber.

"Military officials from the prefectural yamen are here again. They've heard rumors of your presence in Nanking, Lord Liu, and they're searching all houses as usual."

"Try to bribe them," Kuo said immediately. "In my study there are five hundred ounces of gold and five of silver. Simply say we are giving a feast and do not wish the household disturbed."

"That would not be wise," said Chu. "Things have grown

worse, and if they suspect you, Uncle Kuo, your position in Nanking, so valuable to the Red Turbans, would be placed in jeopardy."

"What do you suggest?" said Liu.

Chu knew that his ability to handle such a situation was being tested. "That you permit Han, myself, and Hsu Ta to escort you from the city."

"The gates will be closed at this hour, and by morning the soldiers guarding the city walls will have been instructed to watch for us," said Liu, his calm face expressionless even in danger.

Chu grinned, his eyes alight with the anticipation of adventure. "Hsu Ta and I have some experience in the ways of beggars. I can assure you we will leave Nanking unrecognized."

"Excellent," said Kuo." I will tend to the officials and meet you in the forest beyond the Western Gate at noon tomorrow. My men will be there, ready to escort us up the river to our headquarters near Lake Po-yang."

That night, beneath the fortified tower of the Western Gate, a dozen Mongol soldiers played the Chinese game of dominoes and made fun of four beggars huddled against the wall below. Two of them were merely limping piles of filthy tatters, one appeared to be blind. But the fourth was truly repulsive.

"Do you see that huge fellow down there?" said a soldier, pointing with a torch of lighted pitch. "Blood trickles continuously down his arms from wounds that won't heal. Ugh, the Chinese have strange sicknesses."

When the morning came and the gates opened, the beggars went through.

"Praise Allah," said the soldier to his companions. "We won't have to put up with that wretched fellow any more."

Riding a Tiger

THE FOUR BEGGARS, rags and tatters flying in the wind, raced for the woods to the west of Nanking. When they entered the woods, they moved more cautiously, wary of possible ambush. Chu crept ahead, trusted automatically by the others to keep them safe. His ears were sharpened to every sound, but he heard only the rustling footfall of wild game in the underbrush and the calling of birds. The hot sun of the sixth month filtered through the trees, turning the bamboo leaves to silver and increasing the scent of the pine needles until the air was soft and fragrant.

They came soon to a clearing and found horses tethered to the trees. They were small, sturdy horses from the grasslands of northern Shansi, but Chu saw there was one other, a large black stallion, of the type bred from the Great Horses of Europe and brought to China by the Tartars.

"Kuo took that horse in a raid against a Mongol garrison one night," said Liu, "but he's no use. No one can ride him. Why have you brought that useless animal?" Liu asked the men who began to emerge from their hiding places into the clearing.

"On my orders," said Kuo. He came clumping through the underbrush with a broad grin, having obviously arrived well before the others. Sucking the meat from a piece of deer haunch and wiping the grease on his leather breastplate, he looked much happier now that he had shed his silk robes for soldier's garb again. He gestured toward Chu with the thighbone. "I thought to test the mastery of our large young friend. If he can mount Black Dragon, I will give him my ivory-handled sword. If he survives the first plunge, I will give him bow, arrows, and a leather breastplate."

"What if he masters the horse?" asked Han.

"I will give him the horse," said Kuo.

Chu's eyes gleamed at the thought of possessing such an exquisite animal. He had had little experience with horses, but all of his boyhood he had ridden his father's water buffalo. He knew how to grip the back of an animal with his thighs, how to talk to it, gentle it with voice and hands. Now there were many men watching him. Chu dared not fail.

His courage served him well. Twenty times he was thrown from the back of the plunging horse, but on the twenty-first time Chu remounted, the stallion stood still. Black Dragon accepted his master.

A shout of admiration came from the men.

"We will ride through the foothills," said Kuo. "It will be faster."

"But much less safe," said Chu quietly. "It might be

better if we traveled along the lakes and marshes of the river's edge. I know the way well, and I've also seen that the Mongols don't know how to manage their horses properly in such country."

"You think clearly," Kuo agreed, ordering the men to mount. As they rode, Kuo spoke of other bandit heroes of the past. "Do you know of the legendary hero Sung Chiang? He was chieftain one hundred years ago of the bandit brotherhood of Mt. Liang. The people of the western provinces still remember how he stole from the rich and gave to the poor."

Chu laughed. "We are about to do the same," he said. "We will steal China from the rich Tartars and give it back to the poor Chinese."

At the end of the first day, Chu said, "May I suggest that we do not stop tonight? It would be safer to rest in the morning, and thereafter travel only at night."

It was so decided, and the group went on, Lord Liu riding ahead with his captain, Kuo, behind him and then the lieutenants, Chu and Han. In such an arrangement Chu soon saw danger.

"With your permission, I will send Hsu Ta ahead with outriders, and I myself will ride in front of you, General Liu," he suggested. "I would also like to fan out the rest of the men for protection. Riding this way, if we are attacked, you who are irreplaceable, would be the first to fall."

Liu smiled his slow, rare smile. "I begin to wonder these days, Young Beggar, just which one among us is the most irreplaceable."

Understanding the General's compliment, the men began to laugh, and from then on often referred to Chu among themselves as Beggar Wang, the King of Beggars.

By night they traveled southwest along the Yangtze River. Ghostly nets of mist difted over the marshy ground and over the midriver islands of willows. Bamboo and briars grew in disorderly profusion on the banks, and now and then an aged and twisted plum tree grew between some rocks. Sometimes through the mists they saw a lonely fisherman in his boat, but few people dared to brave the night.

By day, they sought haven in a farmer's hut or at a village inn.

"You see how easy it is to live off the land?" asked Kuo. He winked conspiratorially as he emptied cups of rice beer into his huge stomach, and ate his fill of pork and rice and water chestnuts cooked in soya.

"We ought to pay them for everything," said Chu calmly.

The peasants stared in disbelief when strings of cash were handed out. Who was this outlaw who spoke to them with courtesy and wanted to pay for things instead of stealing them? Word spread quickly along the river, and soon the rebels were greeted with trust and loyalty instead of hopeless fear.

"A most prudent humanity," said Liu in approval.

"I have eaten bitterness myself," replied Chu.

At the border of Anhui province, before they entered Kiangsi, Hsu Ta galloped back to the main party. "Mongols!" he cried. "Ride for the hills!"

"Yes," said Kuo, who was beginning to feel too old to fight unless it was absolutely necessary or unless the attack were well planned beforehand, "to the hills."

Screams of pain from the advance riders warned Chu that it was too late for flight. "Take Liu and Kuo back under those willow trees," Chu said quickly to Han. "If you will defend them there, I will do what I can against the Mongols."

Han nodded and led Liu and Kuo to the safety of the trees.

Chu gave his orders to the men. "We'll use one of their own tricks against them. We'll divide, ride on them separately, and unite at the moment of battle. How many are there, Hsu Ta?"

"Forty or so."

"We are half that number, but we know better than they how to use the river as an ally."

"We?" said Hsu Ta, grinning in the darkness. "You mean *you* do."

"Listen to me then." Chu outlined his plan.

Hsu Ta nodded; taking half the band, Chu rode inland to circle around behind the Mongol soldiers. Those on foot he left with Hsu Ta, their bows drawn and their quivers full of arrows.

To ride through the treacherous marshes wasn't easy, but Chu knew the land and guided Black Dragon where the rest could follow. At the moment he heard the first war cry and knew that Hsu Ta's men had been attacked, he plunged forward.

Within seconds after Hsu Ta had sped the first arrow into the neck of a Mongol soldier, Chu and his followers attacked with their swords from behind. Chu's sword flashed as he severed a Mongol head and then plunged the blade into a Mongol back. Confused by the divided attack, Mongol horses wheeled in an effort to protect themselves on both sides. Over and over again, Chu saw Hsu Ta reach for an arrow, lock his fingers around his bow, and let fly the shaft with unerring accuracy. His men, ranged in a line to block the enemy from breaking through, took their cue from Hsu Ta, and the air was filled with a rain of arrows.

Chu's horsemen plunged in for close hand-to-hand combat. Chu's sword found its way through armor, helmets, and shields as he felled the three nearest men. A Mongol in front of him had left his back unguarded. The man wheeled around, but not in time to escape Chu's death blow. As he fell from his horse, there was an ugly strangling sound of death and terror.

The air rang with the crash of steel and the frightened screams of horses and men. Chu paused only a second to analyse their progress, but it was time enough to feel a blow on the shoulder. Luckily it had been dealt with the side of the sword, but there was no room for him to turn to ward off the next blow. As Black Dragon reared, there was suddenly someone else at Chu's side. Raising his sword arm, Han killed the soldier who would have killed Chu.

"Be more careful," said Han with a smile. "We need you."

The thought of Ma Hou entered Chu's mind. Han had saved his life, yet Chu loved the girl Han was to marry.

But this was hardly the time for personal matters. Chu sought and found Hsu Ta, who had fallen back near the willows to defend Liu. Kuo had long since joined the fighting, and was ably leading those on foot to attack with sword thrusts at legs and mounts and dehorse those Mongols on the edge of the melee. It was Hsu Ta who was in trouble. Three of the enemy were riding against him. He could not fire arrows at so many before they were upon him. Chu wheeled his horse and raced toward the Mongols. As Hsu Ta felled one, his neck pierced with the shaft of the arrow, Chu challenged the other two.

"You will deal with me!" he cried out.

One of the two paled at the sight of the huge, furious giant riding upon them and sped away. The other, evidently an officer, laughed arrogantly.

"And who are you, you Chinese beggar, to deal with a descendant of Genghis Khan's Golden Horde?"

"My name is Chu, Lieutenant under General Liu, of the Red Turbans," Chu returned, his glance proud, his eyes cold with anger. "But you will not live to speak of me or tell your barbarous people who killed you tonight."

"Chu," taunted the Mongol slowly. "Isn't that a word with the same sound as *pig?*"

"Make ready to be shamed before you join your ancestors," Chu's voice lashed out.

He raised his sword and rode in fury against the Mongol. The Mongol was well trained, and as they fought Chu began to understand how two hundred thousand such men could have won against many times that number. The Mongol was a worthy opponent even for Chu. They fought on, neither winning, neither giving ground. It was the

Mongol's inability to cope with the marshy ground that gave Chu an instant's advantage. For a moment, the Mongol's horse stumbled, and in that moment, as he struggled to regain his balance, Chu raised his sword arm and severed his opponent nearly in two.

Breathing heavily, but refusing to recognize his fatigue, Chu turned to Hsu Ta. "Let us drive them into the river."

Hsu Ta mounted the Mongol's horse and rode back to the place where the majority of men on both sides were still fighting. With a word here and there, Chu ordered his men to stay as much to the outside as possible, crowding the Mongols against the river's edge. Chu was everywhere then, and his men with him, fighting with fury and brilliance, making the Mongols fall further and further back. By the first light of dawn, they had all been killed or driven into the river to drown. Only three Red Turbans were numbered among the dead.

"Your military ability and courage saved us, young Chu," said Liu, emerging calmly from the sanctuary of the willows. "Such merit deserves reward and I hereby appoint you to a captaincy."

"You are right to do so," said Kuo ruefully, accepting with good nature Chu's rise to a position equal to his own. "Had you listened to me, we would have been massacred racing for the hills."

"It was your wisdom to bring Chu to me in the first place. Furthermore, I am well aware that no one knows better than you the way to take a walled town. For the gift of Chu and for taking Hua Shan, I give you the rank of Generalissimo."

"But that is a rank like your own," gasped Kuo, who venerated the older man and could not be comfortable with equal rank.

Liu waved a long, thin hand. "You have called me Lord Liu. Continue to do so."

All kowtowed to each other, and then Chu raised his eyes and looked to the river. There he saw a strange and ghostly sight. In an utterly silent line on the river bank, stood a row of poor, hempen-clad figures. With their hands tucked politely in their sleeves, they bowed to the men. The spokesman, a village elder, came forward and bowed again. He spoke to all, but it was Chu he looked at.

"Honored Sirs, we will attend to the bodies of the Mongol soldiers. If they are found here by the enemy garrison down the river, you will be followed and attacked again. You must lose no time in leaving this place. We will bury these bodies, and in the next village, already fishing nets have been spread to catch the dead who have floated downstream."

Chu understood that these men might be sacrificing their lives. If they were caught helping the rebels, their lives and those of their families would be taken. He hesitated.

"Accept our offer," the Elder urged with dignity. "You, who have begun to give us back our pride, must take what little we have to give in return."

"We accept, gratefully," answered Chu. "But remember. He who rides a tiger—"

"—cannot dismount when he pleases," said the Elder, smiling. "We know."

"Already he wins the love and the help of the people," said Liu. "He is right and we have been wrong."

That day, the band of rebels rested in a nearby village. The next night they rode on, over the border into the province of Kiangsi. Here they were not more than a few days journey from Lake Po-yang.

As they finally approached the bandit stronghold, Chu was full of excitement. All his life, he had heard about Po-yang, and now he saw that it was indeed as the story-tellers had described. The village, with a high-walled fortress in its center, was surrounded by a lake of reeds. For miles around waterweed and rushes made a baffling marshland of hidden creeks and paths and secret water-ways, where Mongol troops could be disastrously am-bushed by the bandits, who knew every inch of the treacherous fens. Beyond the marshes to the south, stood still another fortress, the inner stronghold of the brigands. It was placed high in the hills, surrounded by peaks and overhanging cliffs that formed an impregnable wall. The twisting approaches to this fortress were protected by traps the bandits had set—boulders positioned ready to be let loose on intruders and potential avalanches of heavy logs ready to roll down and crush unwanted visitors. Between the outer lair in the marshes and the inner sanctuary of the mountain fortress, the bands of outlaws recruited by the Red Turbans were safe.

Armed guides came forward through the marshes to escort the party to the village.

"Welcome, Venerable Master." They bowed to Liu, and to Kuo and Han, but their faces turned instantly after toward Chu. Obviously, the stories of his exploits in getting Liu out of Hangchow under the very eyes of the Mongols and later destroying a band of Mongol troops had already reached Po-yang.

From the outlying huts and from behind the fortified walls, the men spilled out to see him. Little touched the souls of these brigands, toughened by their lives of pil-laging, drinking, and brawling, but as they pressed near Chu in their red scarves and soldiers' boots, it was obvious to all that they would follow him if he chose to lead. There might be jealousy among the chieftains, but among the common soldiers Chu was a hero.

Someone sent up the cry, "Beggar Wang! Ten thousand years to our King of Beggars!"

Chu bowed and smiled as he rode through the gates, glorying in their cheers. Hsu Ta followed him, obviously proud to serve the young and shining Captain.

Inside the walls, they rode along narrow, twisting streets lined with thatched bamboo and clay houses where the men and the families lived. There were shops, and inns with drinking gardens, and stone warehouses to store millet and rice and smoked pork against days of famine, and other storehouses for booty stolen from Mongols and rich merchant caravans and river barges. Gold and pearls and bales of silk were piled high under the rafters here, and Chu wondered if some of this booty had not found its way into Kuo's pockets as well.

In the center, behind its own walls, were the large spare halls of Liu's Palace of Coolness. Many of the floors were paved with glazed brick, and the sandalwood pillars gave off a delicate fragrance. Chu was surprised to come upon such quiet elegance in so wild a place. In the main hall hung scrolls of exquisite calligraphy, and the library was filled with the books of Classical Wisdom.

"Welcome to my poor home," said Liu with a faint smile at Chu's surprise. "Here there are no pleasure pavilions, no silk-draped dragon boats, but I hope you will be comfortable."

"I have no wish for comfort," said Chu.

"What then?" questioned Lord Liu, taking his place at one end of the long table in the main receiving hall, and indicating chairs for the others.

"There are seventy-two bands here at Po-yang and other bands scattered along the Yangtze River, one hundred thousand followers in all. Many of the band chieftains quarrel among themselves for power and the right to lead raids. Some of the men are skilled at arms and some are untrained. Under you or Generalissimo Kuo they fight well. Without you, they pillage as much as they fight or sprawl about the wine gardens of Po-yang."

"And you wish to discipline them into an army. Is that correct?" asked Liu.

"With your permission," answered Chu.

Liu clapped his hands to have Chu escorted to the guest apartment in the western wing of the house. It was obvious that he intended to think the matter over long and hard before he gave an answer. His own popularity with the men would be as much of a hindrance as a help, Chu reflected ruefully. If those with wisdom, money, and power could not get over petty jealousies, how could lesser leaders? He sighed. The way ahead looked hard, but he would succeed.

Lake Po-Yang

L ORD LIU has consented. You have permission to
train the army."

Chu stared at Kuo. "Finally?"

Chu paced the courtyard in anger. He had been pacing
it for a month, alone except for Hsu Ta and the two maids
assigned to serve him. No one else occupied or visited the
western wing where he had been given rooms, and Chu
had roamed the empty halls and corridors and courts by
himself. In the evenings he walked by the lake and heard
the lonely calls of wild geese through the hanging mists
and the chirping of the crickets. He watched a solitary
crane and the blue kingfishers, or a mated pair of mandarin
ducks in the reeds. He spoke to no one, sensing without
being told, that he was to wait. Often he looked south to
the mountains, but the rocky gorges and silent cliffs seemed
only to echo, "Wait."

He understood it was because he was new among them, and they did not entirely trust him yet. There was that, and, he gradually saw, there was Han. It was Han they wanted to promote, perhaps because they saw, as Chu did, that he could be more easily controlled.

In his rooms Chu sometimes heard the shouts and laughter of men, or the strings of a pipa with the music of bells and drums. And Hsu Ta would say, "Only wait. Lord Liu will send word soon."

"What would I be without you, Hsu Ta," Chu often said.

"The same as you are now," Hsu Ta replied in absolute belief. "A leader of men."

And now, a week after the Autumn Festival on the seventh of the seventh moon, Kuo had come from Lord Liu.

"We needed time to discuss you. And other matters," said Kuo uneasily, as though he hoped fervently that Chu would understand and accept things the way they were.

"Those other matters," said Chu, his eyes searching Kuo's face, "had they to do with setting a time for open attack?"

Kuo signaled to one of the maids to bring him a bamboo chair.

"You are too impatient," sighed Kuo, "too hungry. Lord Liu worries about that."

Chu turned slowly to face Kuo across the lotus pool in the court. "Is it because Lord Liu thinks, and perhaps you also, that I wish power for myself?"

Kuo was startled, Chu could see, and therefore made his face bland. Chu realized he must have been close to the truth.

"No man is without personal ambition," Kuo responded carefully.

"My ambition is to serve the Red Turbans, and through

them, China," said Chu. Why would this man not understand? How often must he explain?

Chu hoped that Kuo understood at least that his anger was simply impatience and no more.

"Lord Liu will set no time for open attack," said Kuo. "Raids will continue. He wishes to know if under these conditions you will undertake to train the men."

"I want first to form an officers' corps. How many chieftains can I depend on?"

"Of the seventy-two bands, all but one has a loyal chieftain."

"He must be sent away. The others I will meet with as soon as possible."

Chu was pleased that Kuo did not question the authority in his voice. If he were to take command of men many of whom were older than he, the tone of his voice and his bearing must make up for his youth. He was amused, though, that once again Kuo seemed startled at his ability to take hold of the situation. Why did they not realize he had done nothing but study and think of these matters for years. But at least there seemed to be no further question that he was to be allowed to handle men, horses, and arms as he wished, and he understood as well that Kuo would back him in any way necessary.

Winter came. The wind from the north was cold and the wild mists swirled over the marshes of Lake Po-yang. The fishermen's boats were gone from the chilled waters of the lake, and only the ancient pines were green.

Despite the cold, Chu gave the men no rest. Archery practice, new skills with the sword, and the training of horses formed only a part of the drill. Using their own mountain fortress and the walls of Po-yang village, Chu taught the men the art of siege. There were war chariots and supply wagons, siege machines and ladders for scaling walls, battering rams and explosive bombs shot from cannon to tear holes and make breaches in the stone, poisoned and flaming arrows, and torches of pitch to create havoc. And there were other methods to make a walled garrison or an occupied town surrender, such as cutting off the water supply by damming rivers or creating fear by spreading rumors of brutality. One thing only there was no need to teach bandits, guerrilla fighting. They already knew well how to separate, move quietly, and ambush an enemy.

But what Chu was most proud of was his officers' corps. Chu realized that organization was something the Chinese could learn from the Mongols. By the time winter came, he had given special training to his officers, from the least of the noncommissioned corporals to those with the highest rank, to lead the men under him. Those with high command, especially, he taught the art of dispersing and working over large areas with their bands only to reassemble for a decisive battle.

"We are far fewer than the Mongols. Strength lies in coordination," Chu insisted. "The old way of simply attacking in separate bands under a single chieftain, without subordinate officers and without plan, will gain us nothing."

"I have been considering a new kind of attack," said Hsu Ta, coming in one afternoon from the cold marshes where the archery targets had been set up.

Chu looked up from his maps and smiled. Hsu Ta was unquestionably his most able officer, and Chu was often able to leave the training of men in tactical maneuvers in his hands. His skill with the bow was still unsurpassed. The longer their friendship lasted, the more Chu had learned to value not only Hsu Ta's skill, but his devotion. Whether it was a matter of restitching Chu's robes and tunics or of teaching Chu's officers, Hsu Ta quietly and eagerly undertook the task.

Hsu Ta sat down and reached for the warm pot of tea. When he had sipped some of the green, fragrant drink he returned Chu's smile.

"Do you trust me enough to confide this new plan of yours?" asked Chu. "Or are you afraid also that I will claim honor for myself." Chu burst out laughing at the expression on Hsu Ta's face. "Don't look so shocked. I'm only teasing. Need we take the 'Peach Garden Oath' of sworn brotherhood like the heroes of ancient Han before you believe that I trust you and know you trust me?"

"Forgive me, I am stupid," said Hsu Ta, grinning, and he brought out the plan, copied out with careful brush strokes on thin paper.

"Let this wait a moment," said Chu, covering the paper with his large hand. "To prove my trust, I will give you a secret that has been troubling me since we were in Nanking."

"Has it to do with the rose jade hidden beneath your inner garments?" asked Hsu Ta. "Don't be angry. I've seen it many times when you take your bath."

Chu nodded. "Kuo's daughter Ma Hou gave it to me."

Hsu Ta looked frightened. "But she is to be betrothed to Han Lin-erh. I've heard Generalissimo Kuo talk about it."

Chu's mouth hardened. "She will not marry Han or anyone else of Kuo's choosing. She is mine."

Hsu Ta said nothing, but Chu could see he was worried. He motioned to the paper and said, "Enough of that. Now, what is your plan?"

Lord Liu sat with Han and Kuo in his own apartments, near a charcoal brazier, wearing the fur-lined outer coat that no longer kept the chill from his aging bones. He looked up as Chu came in.

"You wanted to see me? That means you have decided the time has come for open rebellion!" Chu cried. "The army is ready."

Liu sighed. And in that sigh Chu could hear him thinking that one really should learn to greet his elders properly. He stopped short, bowed, greeted Liu and inquired after his health. It reminded Chu of the days when the Fang Chang had also placed propriety before all. Then he rushed forward again as before, but Liu raised his hand for silence.

"I have no doubt the army is ready, Chu Yuan-chang. But I am not ready. I do not consider that the Red Turbans are yet strong enough to call down the full wrath of Toghan Timur's troops. Remember that they far outnumber us."

"Yes, but they have grown fat and lazy and corrupt living in the Northern Capital. In the south, they die from the heat of summer and malaria. The only troops still lean and disciplined are the garrisons in central China along the Yangtze, and they are few in number," said Chu.

"I do not deny that what you say is true," Liu answered with a calm to match Chu's agitation. "But time and greater strength are still necessary."

"Time can work against us as well," argued Chu. "The Emperor's spies are everywhere, and it won't be long before he uncovers our plans. Then he, too, will begin to train his troops with greater efficiency. He might even send to Mongolia for more troops."

"I have my own sources of information," said Liu in a tone that, though still calm, brooked no further argument. "And I know well that so long as Toghan Timur believes we are simply another of the countless rebel bands pillaging and raiding the southern towns, he will do nothing. Northern China has paid little attention to what was happening in the Yangtze Valley and the south."

"How then do we proceed?" asked Han in his cool, flat voice. Unlike Chu, Han's habit was rarely to argue, always to ask questions.

"We will continue as we were," Liu said quietly, "under the guise of bandits and hiding our military efficiency and numbers, to raid the occupied towns and garrisons. But with this difference. We will attack, not here and there, as before, but with a map under the points of our swords. One province after another our bands will take, not a pocket of territory here and there, but connected territories along the Yangtze, so that for a thousand miles our power will be unassailable. Then, and only then will, we openly declare war on the Mongols."

"And what of rival chieftains?" asked Kuo.

"I have not forgotten them, especially Chang, upriver in the marshes of Lake Tung-ting. He is the one Han worries most about, and quite rightly. His name wields great power already in the province of Hunan. But for the moment, he is more useful than dangerous to us. The people hate him as a plunderer, the Emperor despises him and does nothing, knowing he will never become a real threat to the throne. But because Chang behaves this way, the Emperor believes we all do. Chang is an excellent cover for our purpose."

"And when we no longer need Chang?" questioned Han quietly.

"He will submit to our authority or pay with his life," said Chu, not waiting for Lord Liu to answer.

"To begin," said Liu, "we will start with the province

of Anhui and the approach to the city of Nanking. Bring me the maps."

Throughout the early part of the winter, Chu continued to train the men. Bands were dispatched for small raids in southern Anhui, but never did Liu ask Chu to lead them.

"His preference is for Han, always Han," said Chu bitterly. In his annoyance he pushed away from him the firecrackers he had been making from bamboo sticks and gunpowder for the New Year's Festivities. It was a day in the twelfth moon just before the end of the year.

Rarely did Hsu Ta dare to interrupt Chu in his bitter moods. This time he ventured, "Isn't it possible that he is waiting for you to grow less angry, less impatient? It is my opinion that Lord Liu prefers you to Han at the head of the troops. But he wishes you to learn self-control before sending you to fight."

"I have served Lord Liu's interests well," said Chu furiously.

"I'm sorry. I didn't mean to interfere."

Chu was immediately contrite. "I'm sorry, too, Hsu Ta. Who more than you has the right to speak to me in any way you please. But come. I'm feeling restless. Shall we walk in the mountains together as we used to at Hua Shan?"

Only in the lonely blue-green mountains could Chu find peace. The wind blew cold through the mountain pass and along the long gorges choked with scree and boulders. The pines sang in the wind and the clouds cast shadows on the ground. In the swirling mists Chu prowled the woods and followed the mountain streams to their source, fretting, always fretting, about not being sent to fight.

"I think of the ancient poet Han-shan living on Cold

Mountain," said Chu, pausing to lean against a giant boulder in the center of a gorge. "Do you remember the line, 'Moonlight on Cold Mountain is white silent knowledge.' If I stand here and wait for the moon, will I then learn patience?"

Hsu Ta smiled. "You seem to forget the next line, honored friend. 'The spirit is enlightened of itself.' "

"Then I can learn no more. I have searched my spirit and I find no patience there." Chu's brow darkened. "And that being the case, I will go at once to Lord Liu and tell him so."

"That is asking for trouble," said Hsu Ta.

But Chu had already begun to stride back down the mountain.

"Then trouble is what I will get," his answer floated back on the wind.

The New Year

W ITHOUT SENDING a messenger first to announce his arrival, Chu stormed into Liu's apartments. The knot of his hair had come loose, and the wetness of the mountain mists still clung to his sleeves.

"How many times have I asked you not to burst into my rooms as if you had been blown in by the fury of the Wind Dragon," scolded Liu.

"I cannot learn patience here at Po-yang," muttered Chu, with a hasty bow. "I've tried, and it's no use." His voice grew angrier. "You always send Han to lead the raids, and I can't bear it any longer. Why not me, Honorable Liu? Why?"

Chu felt the anger in Liu's penetrating glance. But this time, instead of politely lowering his eyes before a superior, he stubbornly returned Liu's anger with his own.

"No one dares to question my decisions," said Liu, more sharply than he had ever spoken to Chu before.

"But because you have trained my army, and because in your more sensible moods I look upon you as an adoptive son, I will give you an explanation. I send Han because I can trust him not to go too far. When I order him to take one town and no more, he obeys, as you would not. When I order him to do nothing for a time, he obeys, as you would not."

"True," said Chu. He stopped pacing and sat upon a black lacquer stool near Liu's chair. The passion in his voice deepened, but grew less wild, as he spoke his next thoughts. "I would not obey your words, but your spirit. You wish to conquer the Mongols as much as I do, and that is the thought I would hear and obey."

Liu sat in silence for a moment. When he spoke next, his words came slowly. "I have no doubt that when the time comes, you will be the one to vanquish China's enemies. You will be the greatest general I have ever had, and for that reason, if for no other, I do not want your life endangered in preliminary raids."

"And Han's life?"

"Han Lin-erh does nothing foolish. He would not put himself in danger as you would." A glint of humor came to Liu's eyes. "But there is one thing I have to say that will please you. I have been reading Han's reports on the situation in southern Anhui. He is making excellent progress with small raids and ambushes against the Mongols in the area of Hao-chou, as well as with the infiltration of towns. We will soon be in a position to rebel openly. I have set the time for early spring. Surely you can wait another month or two."

On New Year's Day of 1351, the Mongol Emperor Toghan Timur was thirty-one years old. He had ascended the Dragon Throne at thirteen and had learned nothing since about affairs of state.

"He understands fear, and he understands pleasure, and that is all," his Mongol Ministers complained. "The great Kublai Khan has been dead only sixty years, and already the Empire is falling down around our ears."

The hour was just before dawn, and the Ministers in their court robes were assembled in the Audience Hall for their morning audience with the Emperor.

"Unquestionably Kublai was in many ways the greatest of our Emperors in China," said the Prime Minister, "but he made two mistakes his grandfather the Genghis Khan would not have made. To these two mistakes we now owe many of our troubles. The first mistake was to move the capital from Karakorum to China. With his seat of power so far east, Kublai lost much of central Asia; and now Tamburlaine begins to make his own empire from Samarkand and dreams of taking China for himself. The second mistake arises from the first. In moving his capital to China, it was Kublai's desire to become a true Chinese emperor, a Son of Heaven. He and his court forgot the rough ways and warrior virtues of our Tartar ancestors. Instead he built his city of Cambaluc and the Grand Canal from here to the Yangtze River so that produce might be brought for his pleasure. He insisted that Mongols live according to Confucian virtues, and even wasted his time listening and talking to foreigners like the Big Nose from Italy, Marco Polo. In all this, Kublai taught the Mongols to forget their warrior heritage; and since Kublai's death, the Mongols in China have grown weaker and weaker with each successor to the throne. If I had my way—"

"We know," said the Minister of Rites. "You would act on Genghis Khan's proposal to exterminate all Chinese with the names of Chang, Wang, Liu, Li, and Chow."

"What you seem to forget," the Primer Minister said, his voice full of hate even at the sound of Chinese names, "is that while there are six hundred thousand Mongols, there are sixty million Chinese. They outnumber us one hundred to one, and it is no easy matter to keep such numbers under control. We have forbidden them to wear the colors and emblems of their families, we have forbidden them arms and horses, we have forbidden their societies to meet, we have raised taxes to punish them—but it is not enough. We must teach them to fear us. They must feel the terror of our whips and swords."

In the gray light of dawn, Toghan Timur was carried in his chair to the Audience Hall of the Imperial Palace. As always he peered through the curtains of his litter to

admire the majestic splendor of his imperial capital, the dozens of halls and courts, the soaring yellow-tiled roofs, the carved marble stairs and verandah railings, and his favorite blue-tiled Wall of Nine Dragons. Above all he loved the parks, dotted with artificial lakes and hills and mountains, the plains stocked with animals of the chase, and the exotic trees brought to the park on the backs of elephants from all quarters of the world.

Even more, Toghan Timur preferred his cool and costly summer palace, Shang-tu, where Kublai had built a vast hunting tent of leopard skins trimmed with ermine and sable, with a roof of gilded bamboos, and golden tent poles painted with the dragons of China. From this pleasure house or from the golden howdah on the backs of a pair of elephants, Toghan Timur liked to watch his cheetahs stalk the stags, his hawks swoop upon cranes, his trained tigers fight with bears, boars, or wild cattle.

Toghan Timur sighed fretfully at the thought of his ancestor Kublai. Always Kublai's greatness, his charities, his patronage of scientists and artists, his visitors from everywhere—from Italy and Persia to Korea—were constantly being held up to Toghan Timur by his Ministers as a model to follow. Not by his Prime Minister, of course, who hated the Chinese, but in any case, it was no use. Toghan Timur could not be either like Genghis or like Kublai. He was too afraid of the Chinese to rule them, and because of his fear, he escaped into pleasure.

The Audience Hall was large enough, under its gold and blue carved rafters, to hold a thousand courtiers. Nearly that many, in their silk court robes, embroidered satin shoes, and jeweled or furred caps, were present as Toghan Timur was escorted in his gold imperial robes to the high throne in front of the Dragon Screen. Before him, his Grand Councilors and Ministers and Princes knelt and bowed their heads to the floor.

The Prime Minister, thin-lipped and angry, came forward. "Ten thousand years to our August Son of Heaven," he addressed Toghan Timur. "Reports have reached me that the number of bandits in the south and along the Yangtze River grows each week and that they raid our garrisons almost constantly."

Toghan Timur yawned behind his gold-flecked fan. He wished he had his silver pipe with him and some of the opium newly brought to him from India.

"In Chung-kuo, the Middle Kingdom, there are always earthquakes, floods, famine, and bandits," fretted Toghan Timur. "It is nothing new."

The Prime Minister controlled his anger and continued to speak patiently, as to a child. Thirty-one years old and still a silly, petulant child! "You must send for more Mongol troops, from the steppes, from the Altai mountains in Mongolia, from the Himalayas of Tibet. If we do not hang every rebel soon, it will be too late."

"If I send for troops, they will only fight each other beneath the palace walls on behalf of one party or another. They will be on my side, or your side, or on the side of my son."

The Prime Minister was startled by Toghan Timur's shrewdness in understanding the bitter quarrels for power in the Imperial Palace.

"None the less, Majesty, we must have fresh troops. There are rumors that it will not be long before the bandits break into open rebellion against us."

Toghan Timur was thinking of his breakfast. He did not want to be plagued by China's problems any longer.

"Enough," he said, playing with the green jade button

that fastened his wide-sleeved robe at the throat. "The Audience is ended." And he rose and left the Audience Hall, leaving the Ministers arguing behind him.

"He doesn't understand," said the Minister of Punishments. "The people of south and central China are not the same as those in the north. They do not so easily accept our rule."

The Grand Councilors, the Ministers of the Six Boards, and the Censors agreed.

The Rise of the
Red Turbans

A T L A K E P O - Y A N G , Chu waited restlessly through the New Year's festivities, when everyone wore new clothes, paid old debts, made offerings to the gods, and celebrated with banquets, firecrackers, and processions. Hsu Ta presented Chu with the traditional rice of five colors and an amulet to ward off evil influences. But it was not until the fifteenth of the first moon, on the second day of the Feast of Lanterns, when all the shops, squares, even the narrowest lanes were lit by lanterns painted with landscapes and birds, animals and flowers, and every imaginable sort of scene, that Chu at last received the message from Liu he had waited for so long.

"You will ride east."

In the great hall of his mansion, Liu's voice rang calmly over the silence of his assembled officers. "Under Generalissimo Kuo and Captain Chu, you will ride openly against the Mongols. Use the Hua Shan monastery as your strong-hold, and begin by taking the entire area of Hao-chou in southern Anhui. I have reports from Han Lin-erh that the peasants are with us, and reports from Cambaluc say that Toghan Timur does nothing against us."

In the beginning of the second month, 1351, sixty of the seventy-two bands of well-trained Red Turbans left Lake Po-yang. Among these men were the best archers, the most brilliant horsemen, and the greatest experts in the use of the scimitar and lance in all of China. With no need to pull the heavy siege machines and cannon—Han had those waiting in Anhui—the Red Turbans moved easily through the marshes and uplands of the Yangtze Valley.

Despite the generalship of Kuo, it was Chu they followed. He had lived among them and trained them, until they were no longer quarrelsome groups of bandits with many clan chieftains, but units of a proud, fierce army, all united in a single cause. The men still wore their red scarves and boots, but now each was fitted out with leather armor and the strong raw silk shirts Chu had insisted on. Arrows did not penetrate such material, but drove the silk into the wound, so that their surgeons simply pulled the silk to dislodge the arrowhead.

Chu rode at the head of his army. Over his own raw silk shirt and leather breastplate he wore a vermilion coat trimmed with sable and buttoned at the throat with jasper. In the soft sunlight of early spring, he rode on the back of Black Dragon, great and powerful, like the legendary heroes of the ancient Han.

Only one matter troubled Chu as he rode toward Anhui, and that was the thought of Han Lin-erh. Only on the fact that China must be rid of Mongol rule did they agree. On all else they were divided. And then there was Ma Hou.

He fingered the piece of rose jade on its silk cord.

"You are going to have to tell Han soon that you want Ma Hou for your own wife," said Hsu Ta, riding beside Chu.

"It's strange," said Chu. "Han thinks I want to rule China someday, but he doesn't know I want Ma Hou. I wish there were some way I could tell him how gladly I would trade the throne for Ma Hou."

"I think you could tell him," said Hsu Ta thoughtfully. "I think he would be equally glad to make the exchange."

At the Hua Shan monastery, Han waited with his troops for Kuo and Chu. The siege towers, battering rams, cannon, and explosives were ready. The walled town of Hao-chou was quiet, as yet unaware that it faced attack.

Kuo and Chu arrived with their silently moving column late one night at the beginning of the third month. Han was waiting and escorted them both to his quarters in the southern wing of the residence hall.

"I have been thinking," said Chu, "it is very near the Ching-ming Festival. Everyone will be busy paying respects to the dead. A good day to attack, do you agree?"

"I agree," said Kuo. By now he was used to Chu making most of the decisions for the army. He was grateful to be left in peace to enjoy his wine and his business transactions.

Chu noticed that Han seemed startled and angry at Chu's newly gained position of authority.

But open quarreling was not Han's way. He therefore said only, "We will discuss it by all means. I have been in Anhui for some time, and I understand the situation."

Kuo raised a hand to ward off further discussion. "Whatever you both decide is all right with me. I will fight gladly, but don't involve me in the planning." Kuo looked around for Han's retainers. "Will something to eat be brought soon? I've been riding all day, and I'm hungry."

"Forgive me," said Han politely and clapped his hands for the servants.

Dinner—of fish soup, mutton served with rice, honey fritters, and several kinds of cake—was exquisite. Han had even managed to get hold of White Cloud tea and an excellent rice wine. Whatever Han did, thought Chu, he did elegantly, and thinking of Ma Hou, he could not help but compare the fashionable, handsome young man with his own awkward roughness.

There was no further discussion about the day of attack. Han could not but agree that the Ching-ming, the Festival of the Dead, on the fifth of the third month, was an excellent choice. It was the chief spring festival, and the townspeople would be busy repairing and cleaning graves, and placing offerings before ancestral tablets. Afterwards there would be picnics and feasting, processions of costumed dancers and musicians, and moon-viewing parties. Since traditionally even soldiers were excused from duty on that day, no one would be expecting an attack.

The Red Turbans descended the Hua Shan mountain at dawn. The heavy cavalry rode first, then the light cavalry. The infantry came behind, with the wagons of supplies, the spare horses, and the great siege towers and cannon. It was their first open advance on the Mongols, and the men were excited. The hooves of their horses pounded the earth, and their shouts and cries created a sensation among the peasants in the villages they passed. Many of the farmers stayed to follow the soldiers, and to them Chu shouted his proclamation, summoning the Chinese to rise against the Mongols.

"These barbarians are created to obey and not to command a civilized nation."

Wherever they rode, Chu realized that the people responded with universal exultation. For the first time in a thousand years, the Chinese nation was not on the defensive against a barbarian attack, but was itself advancing to attack the enemy. The towns supplied money, the women brought their jewelry and hair ornaments. Chu's men were received with enthusiasm, and in towns where there were few Mongols to prevent it, they opened their gates readily. In the province of Anhui, the people had had enough of the Mongols, and even the merchants and some of the gentry were willing to risk the possibility of Mongol reprisal to prove their loyalty to the Red Turbans. In their turn, the Red Turbans behaved. Chu had forbidden them to plunder, and he saw to it that discipline was maintained.

Toward evening, they approached the walls of Hao-chou.

"With a good rest tonight," said Han, "the men will be ready to attack in the morning."

"They are ready now," said Chu. "After the winter's training I have given them, it would take more than a day's ride to wear them down. There is a large Mongol garrison here, and Hao-chou is well fortified. We shall need surprise tactics to take this city, and one such tactic is a night attack. They will hardly expect it."

Kuo nodded from his horse, and Han had no choice but to agree. Thin-lipped with jealous anger he would not speak, he rode to give the order.

"I grow less and less worried about the Mongols, and more and more worried about Han," said Hsu Ta. "His envy of you increases each day."

"I will win China for him to rule," said Chu, smiling. "Perhaps his humor will improve."

"Look!" cried Hsu Ta, suddenly gaping at the crenelated ramparts of the city. Everywhere there were Mongols ranged along the walls. "There must be thousands of them," Hsu Ta gasped.

"Well, what did you expect?" bellowed Kuo, his excitement rising at the call to battle like an ancient warhorse.

"Light cavalry forward," ordered Chu.

Hsu Ta led his three ranks of mounted archers from behind the two ranks of heavy cavalry forward into the open field before the city walls. Flight after flight of arrows rained through the evening to push the Mongols off the ramparts long enough for the siege towers, battering rams, and cannon to be brought forward. As the infantry rolled the heavy equipment toward the walls, the city gates opened just long enough for a regiment of a thousand men to pour through. It was the Mongol heavy cavalry, and Chu led his cavalry to meet it. In hand to hand combat with scimitars, battle-axes, and short swords, the two mounted troops clashed, while Hsu Ta's archers continued their volley of arrows against the Mongols on the ramparts. From the walls and towers, the Mongols flung burning balls of pitch and shot flaming arrows into the advancing infantry under Han.

"Take the left flank and go round to the north gate," Chu commanded Kuo. Without stopping to think that he outranked Chu, Kuo obeyed. It had the immediate effect of drawing away the Mongol archers on the walls, many of whom raced along the ramparts to bring word to the defense troops at the back of the city. It was clear that the Mongols were less prepared than usual for an attack.

Chu's cavalry was having little trouble with the Mongol horsemen. They put up only a short fight before racing for the city's gates. Chu's men pursued them, slaughtering those in the rear. But many made it back to the gates, which swung open to receive them. As the last of the

Mongols raced in, and Chu and his cavalry reached the gates, hot oil and burning pitch rained down. Chu and his men were forced to stop short, unable to pursue the Mongols through their gate. Meanwhile Hsu Ta's archers found targets in hundreds of Mongols, but always more took their places and made it impossible for Han to get close with the siege machinery.

"Enough," commanded Chu. "We will attack again in the morning."

"I can bring the cannon closer," said Han. "Why not fire explosives throughout the night?"

"I don't want the city's population hurt if possible," Chu answered. "When Genghis Khan came to China, he left cities in smoking ruins and depopulated towns wherever he rode. Forty million Chinese died in those years. It would be better if the people thought of us as liberators, not as murderers."

Han raised delicate eyebrows. "And how, may I ask, do you expect to take Hao-chou without attacking it?"

"We will attack the walls and the Mongols that swarm them, not the people of the city," said Chu sharply.

Han argued no more.

Before the morning mists had risen, in the first flush of dawn, Chu ordered a fresh attack. Again Hsu Ta's archers shot volley after volley of arrows at the Mongols on the ramparts and towers. Again Chu led his cavalry against the mounted enemy who raced through the open gate. And again Kuo made diversionary attacks at the north gate. This time, Han managed to get two siege towers in place and several scaling ladders. His infantry even scaled the wall in several places. But always they were shot down, and fell screaming to earth. The battle went on without letup until early afternoon.

As the leaders met briefly in an officer's tent, Han looked exhausted and Hsu Ta worried openly.

Kuo was his cheerful self, but even he remarked, "The more Mongols I shoot, the more swarm up the walls to take their places. Our couriers must have misjudged their numbers."

Only Chu was calm.

"No matter. The time has come to retreat."

At Hsu Ta's disappointment, Kuo's relief, and the thinly veiled contempt on Han's face, Chu gave his great laugh.

"A Mongolian tactic, practiced by Genghis Khan. You will see what happens. First each of us will go back to his troops. I will signal with flags that a relief army is on the way from Liu. The minute you read the signal, which of course will be read equally well by the Mongols, I want to see the most rapid retreat you have ever executed. Not a single piece of baggage, not one war machine, not a supply wagon or a cannon do I want collected. You may even ask some of your men to drop swords and arrow quivers and bows as they race away."

Han no longer veiled his contempt. "It is impossible, what you suggest. Red Turbans do not run for cover. They will lose face. They would rather die than be thought cowards. No one will obey you."

Chu's voice sharpened in command, and in his eyes was a look no one dared disobey. "You will do as I ask immediately. I do not wish to wait until the Mongols decide to take Chinese citizens of Hao-chou as hostages to insure our surrender. But perhaps you disagree?"

Han said nothing. There was nothing to say. He turned immediately to leave the tent.

"You have a plan of course," said Hsu Ta quietly.

"Of course," said Chu, nodding.

"Good," said Kuo cheerfully. "It shall all be done as you say."

The leaders returned to their men. Chu ordered several of his field officers to begin signaling with their flags. Shortly after, Chu raised the siege of Hao-chou and commanded the most rapid retreat the startled Mongols had ever seen. Chu watched them staring down on the field, shocked as the Red Turbans fled, leaving equipment, tents, baggage, and everything behind them. Chu led the withdrawal throughout the entire night. In the morning, he stopped the army cold.

"Ride," shouted Chu. "Ride as fast as your horses will go."

"Ride where?" yelled Kuo over the confusion of the murmuring men.

"Back to Hao-chou!" commanded Chu.

The army turned and raced back, covering the same distance in less than half the time.

When they reached the battlefield under the walls of Hao-chou, Chu gave a great exultant cry. It was all just as he had expected; nearly the entire Mongol garrison was plundering his abandoned camp, and all the city gates stood wide open. With the Red Turbans behind him, Chu rode down upon the looters. They were so busy collecting and fighting over the goods the Red Turbans had left behind, they were completely incapable of organizing themselves for battle. In mad confusion they tried to reach their horses, form combat groups, and defend themselves, but it was no use. In panic they trampled each other and their terrified screams were deafening as Chu's men encircled and slaughtered them.

When the Mongols on the field had fled or been killed, and Chu's men had ridden through the open gates and taken the remaining enemy troops by storm, a great shout rose from the army.

In their first open battle against the Mongols, the Chinese had won a decisive and resounding victory. They had regained all of their own supplies and added Mongol horses and equipment as well.

"One small city recovered," said Hsu Ta. "Only ten thousand more to go."

Han and Chu

I T W A S H A N who led the victory procession through
the streets of the city of Hao-chou, and it was Han
who was received by the Magistrate and the rich gentry
officials of the district, with all the honors due to a liberating hero. Kuo, carrying the Red Turban banner, rode
at Han's side and hoped that the grand reception also
included a banquet, a silk-covered bed, and entertainment
by pretty singing girls.

Chu remained with his army outside the city walls.
When he had seen to it that the surgeons attended the
wounded, that the dead were buried, that all arms were
collected, he gave orders for the tents to be set up so
the men might rest.

It was early evening when everything was settled.

"Come," Chu said to Hsu Ta. "We have ridden and
fought and worked enough for a time. Let's walk in those

woods beyond the field. There will be a stream where we can bathe. Afterwards we will see which of us is the best archer. Whoever brings down a deer or a wild pig or a pheasant for dinner wins, and the other must cook it for both."

Hsu Ta fell in with Chu's long strides, but on his face was a gloomy frown.

"There is enough resentment in your eyes to fill the depths of the Eastern Sea," said Chu. "What's the matter?"

"Matter?" grumbled Hsu Ta. "No matter. Only that by now Han has been glorified and fussed over by every rich mandarin in the city. From the highest official of three degrees to the lowest official of one degree, all will be honoring him with kowtows, with invitations to banquets and parties, to say nothing of costly gifts of silk and jade girdles and pearls, silver goblets and ingots of yellow gold." As Hsu Ta recited the lists of treasure, he grew angrier and angrier.

The sight of his small friend growing furious over such nonsense made Chu burst out laughing. "Do not forget the pleasures of airy guest halls, or drifting about a spring garden lake in a dragon boat composing poems in the ancient manner to the moon, or sleeping on a soft bed under covers in four shades of silk. And then of course there are the singing girls with small Golden Lily feet, and landscape scrolls to admire, and games to play."

At Chu's teasing, Hsu Ta grew more furious than ever. "You don't understand. I'm not discussing insignificant trifles. I'm angry only because you have won the city, but it is Han who receives the honor." Hsu Ta paused and flushed, as if he hesitated to say all that was in his mind.

"Speak," said Chu, this time without laughter, for he saw that Hsu Ta was truly upset. "You know you may say anything to me you like without fearing my anger."

Hsu Ta dropped to his knees. "In making way for Han, you lose face before the men," Hsu Ta whispered.

Chu bent down and raised Hsu Ta to his feet. "Thank you for the love which permitted you to say such words," answered Chu in a gentle tone. "Do the men speak of this?"

"Yes," said Hsu Ta miserably. "And on their own behalf they grumble at having to encamp outside the walls instead of being allowed to enjoy the pleasure of Purple Stone Street in the Gay Quarters of the city. You will not let them plunder, but they feel the least you could do is permit them a little fun."

Chu laughed again. "I see. It is not really my losing face they worry about. It is their loss of pleasure that concerns them. Hsu Ta, my friend, you worry too much. I will explain my reasons for remaining outside the city, and then you will understand. For the men, it is simple. I don't want them to grow soft and lazy, to forget that they are warriors. That happens easily to a victorious army. For myself, it is more complicated, but the most important reason is this: I have no interest in being a great lord, as I think Han does. I do not believe he had this idea from the first. I think he was a man without ordinary passions of any kind; but then, encouraged by Liu and Kuo, he began to develop, under the coolness of his manner, the most burning passion of all: the desire to rule other men. I have no such desire, and since I think Han will govern wisely and with justice, I see no reason why he should not be the one to receive Hao-chou's honors."

"Then I suppose there is no more to say," responded Hsu Ta.

A swift glance at Hsu Ta convinced Chu that all was not yet well in his friend's mind. "Still, you seem to have more to say. Come, you may as well tell me everything."

"It is only that I worry about Han's feelings toward you. Always he has envied you. The men follow you, not him, and he knows it. And if you now give him power, and he feels he owes it to you, he may begin to hate you for such an obligation, or perhaps fear you as a constant rival. He is a strange and silent man. It is difficult to know his thoughts. But I worry—"

Chu clapped his hand over Hsu Ta's mouth. "Enough worry for one evening. Look how beautiful that wisteria is, and that purple flowering sedge."

The air of the spring evening was sweet in the forest as they rambled through the brush under the trees. In a glen, an unbroken mass of flowers nodded fragrantly before the breeze, and beyond, a small waterfall spilled into a clear pool beneath silver overhanging willow trees. Chu and Hsu Ta bathed, and then with their bows and arrows and short daggers tucked into their belts, went off through the woods to hunt for dinner. When a deer crossed their path, running at full speed, Hsu Ta's arrow missed him narrowly. Chu raised his long yellow bow and let his arrow fly. The deer fell instantly to the ground.

"I am the best archer in all of China," grumbled Hsu Ta good-naturedly, "and already you surpass me."

"My arms are longer, that is all," said Chu with a broad grin.

"And because of such a trifling accident of birth, I am the one to cook dinner," sighed Hsu Ta in mock vexation. "The Jade Emperor in Heaven has not dealt with me fairly."

"We share the command and the responsibility, and I say no!" Han's voice was cold with anger as he strode across the polished stone floor of his Hall of Reception. Kuo sat wearily at the long table, fatter and more slovenly than ever, but less cheerful. The pains in his stomach, which in the past had only bothered him now and then, had lately been getting worse. And the constant battle between Chu and Han, with himself as advisor and intermediary, only served to make him feel more ill. Kuo had sent couriers to Lord Liu at Lake Po-yang, but Liu's answers were always the same.

"I will attend to matters in the province of Kiangsi. You must attend to those in Anhui. You are the Generalissimo. You decide what must be done."

Only Kuo no longer wished to make decisions. For two years now, Han had governed from Hao-chou, while Chu led raids against the Mongols from his camp outside the city walls. In all of Anhui south of the Yangtze, not one town, village, or mountain fortress remained in Mongol hands. Now Chu wished to strike camp and leave the area altogether, to cross to the left bank of the river and take the northern part of the province as well.

"I refuse to agree," said Han.

Chu said nothing. He simply rose and left. The army was his. It would do what he said, what he wanted. And Han knew it. That perhaps was at least part of the trouble.

Later, pacing his huge but portable tent, Chu looked up in consternation as Kuo entered. Kuo had come, as usual, with soothing words, words of conciliation, but all Chu could think about was how ill Kuo looked.

"Please lie down," said Chu, leading Kuo to his own bed under the fine mesh insect netting.

Under Chu's obvious concern and affection, the sick man for the first time let his staunch shoulders and the great barrel of his chest and belly slump, until he looked less like a robust soldier in his prime and more like a fat, aging man. He sat on the edge of Chu's bed, breathing hard and holding his stomach.

Chu nodded to Hsu Ta, who hurried off to call a doctor.

"I want a fortune-teller and priests," mumbled Kuo.

"Yes, yes, you shall have everything necessary," said Chu. His own faith was in Doctor Chow, who had taken his degree at the National University School of Medicine in Hangchow and then, refusing to serve the Mongols, had joined the Red Turbans. But Kuo still clung to the old superstitions, and to ease his mind, Chu sent a retainer for a Tao priest from the Jade Emperor's Temple and for a Buddhist monk from the nearby Cloister of Earthy Seclusion. Fortune-tellers were easy to find. There were several within his own camp ministering cures, amulets, and spells to the soldiers.

It was the fortune-teller who arrived first at Kuo's bedside.

"*Amitofo!*" he cried out when he saw the sick man. "It is obvious you have been ignoring all the elementary taboos and have not observed lucky and unlucky days of the calendar. Have you forgotten that all things in the universe affect one another and that you must not make any important moves or decisions without a proper reading of the signs and numbers? Now, in what hour, day, month, and year were you born?"

After Kuo had answered these questions, the fortune-teller cast his rice straws, examined the pattern they made, and consulted his Book of Changes. He consulted also the imperial calendar. He made notes and handed Kuo a list of lucky days and directions for various activities such as bathing, fasting, and traveling. Then he searched through his purse and handed Kuo a small piece of green jade on which was carved a magic formula from the Tantra. "Hang this over your door for thirty-three days. It will bring back into balance the *yin* and *yang,* the weak and strong principles inside you. Do this, and observe the lucky days. Then you will be cured."

"It will take that long?" said Kuo, falling back against the pillow. *"Ai-ya!"*

The monk and priest arrived next. Both of them insisted immediately that evil spirits had taken hold of Kuo.

"The human body is like the universe," the Tao priest explained. "When its five elements, water, fire, wood, metal, and earth, which correspond to the five essential organs and five openings of the body, are disturbed, there is chaos and illness."

"You are forgetting the disturbance of the five breaths,

warm, cold, dry, moist, and fiery, which must circulate well throughout the body for health, and the *yin,* the female or cold principle, and *yang,* the male or warm principle, which must be balanced," said the monk.

"You may also be ill from too much of one of the seven feelings," argued the priest. "Too much joy, anger, sadness, fear, love, hate, or desire."

"Enough," Chu suddenly interrupted as Doctor Chow entered the tent. "Here are four ounces of silver. Pray for Generalissimo Kuo and have services read in your temples."

Doctor Chow examined Kuo quietly for several minutes, especially his face and the twelve pulses. Then he inquired carefully about Kuo's symptoms.

"The last time I was examined," said Kuo helpfully, "I was given pills of combined crushed spiders, crushed pearls, and the powder made from a dog fly whose wings and legs had been removed."

"Excellent," said Doctor Chow with a comforting smile. "Now please rest quietly for a while."

Doctor Chow drew Chu aside. "The pains in his stomach are simply due to worry and overeating. The real trouble is his heart. I can give him medicine to ease his stomach, but for the rest, he should go home to Nanking and spend his life quietly."

"How long can he live?" Chu asked.

"A year or two with care and rest," answered Doctor Chow. "Otherwise . . ." The doctor left off and shrugged.

"Bring the pills to ease his stomach," said Chu. "I will talk to him."

Chu brought a low stool and sat next to Kuo, whose once cheerful face now stared at Chu with frightened eyes.

"Has the time come for me to Ascend the Dragon? How soon do I join my ancestors?"

"They will have to wait for you a good while longer," said Chu, smiling to hide his worry from Kuo. "Doctor Chow says you have only been eating too much and pouring too much rice wine down your throat. He is bringing stomach medicine for you, but in the meantime I have a request to make. I want you to organize the infiltration of Nanking. Only you can do this, because you are well known and respected there, and the Mongols do not suspect that you are anything but a rich merchant. Go there, and by buying appointments for them, begin to place friends who are sympathetic to our cause in important official positions. Then when the time comes, it will not be so difficult for us to take the city."

Kuo's face brightened immediately. It was obvious that his mind was relieved about his physical condition. It was also clear that he would not miss riding his horse or creeping through the marshes or hiding in mountain passes to attack Mongols. Yet to save face, he protested loudly. "It will mean I shall have to bathe and wear city gowns."

"I beg you to make the sacrifice," said Chu in a serious voice, noting with pleasure the look of relief on Kuo's face.

When Kuo had left, accompanied by a carefully chosen group of outriders and an escort of guerrilla-trained bodyguards, Chu breathed more freely.

"Actually, he may be of great help in Nanking," Chu said to Hsu Ta.

Each was leaning against a supporting bamboo pole in the open doorway of Chu's tent. Chu saw that, as usual, Hsu Ta looked worried.

"Well, what is it now?"

"Lord Liu is back at Lake Po-yang. Kuo is on his way to Nanking. That means there is no one here to make you behave, and you will do exactly as you please in disregarding Han's refusal to let you go. Am I right?"

"You are right," said Chu, stepping away from the tent to arch his great muscular body under the freedom of a brilliant blue sky.

"That is what I thought," said Hsu Ta promptly, "and that's why I'm worried."

Five Gates

A FTER TWO MONTHS of preparation, Chu
decamped in the summer of 1353.

With Hsu Ta and several officers, he went to pay his
respects to Han in the Governor's Mansion. Han sat in
cold silence, fingering the sleeve of his embroidered robe
of office. He had received a formal appointment from
Liu as Governor of Hao-chou. He did not rise as Chu
entered. In front of his own retainers and Chu's officers,
Han had every intention of maintaining the dignity and
authority of his position.

Chu understood immediately. Therefore, instead of announcing his departure, he kowtowed and craved permission.

"Ten thousand-fold happiness to the Governor," Chu
greeted Han on his knees.

Han nodded stiffly, "You have a petition?"

"The army is ready. We beg permission to depart."

"How many men do you leave to protect Hao-chou and its Governor?"

"You have five thousand men in your own command. I leave you an additional ten thousand. They have already been garrisoned, as of this morning, within these walls."

"That is not enough," said Han sharply.

Chu clenched his teeth for a minute to help him keep his temper. Would the time never come when he no longer had to struggle against the very men whose kingdom he wanted to save? For the moment, he managed to conquer his anger and explain. "There are no Mongols left in the vicinity. Should fresh troops be sent south by the Emperor to this area, I shall personally return to defend you."

After a moment of silence, Han made a gesture of dismissal with a long, pale hand. "Go," he said, the small, handsome mouth turned sullenly down at the corners.

And yet, Chu thought as he strode from the hall, perhaps his departure would be a relief to Han. With Chu gone, Han's power in southern Anhui would be absolute.

The Red Turban army moved north that night. Like a great dragon uncoiling from sleep, it stretched and rose, and its weight made a great thundering sound on the earth of China. But it was a dragon even the most fearful Chinese farmers did not fear, because its head was Chu Yuan-chang, the King of Beggars, and the fire that breathed from its mouth would not so much as singe a single hair on a Chinese head. The flames of its tongue licked only Mongols, people said. For the Chinese, there was warmth, not danger, against the curve of the dragon's belly.

As Chu rode before his troops, no one remembered that officially his rank was that of Captain. To the men he was a king. Their eyes never tired of seeing him. And they could hardly help do that since he wore a red robe over his armor. All who needed him could find him, on the battlefield or as the army moved.

It was something Hsu Ta argued hotly with Chu about.

"Will you please take that robe off. On the battlefield you make a perfect target for those pigs."

"I am so large, they would find me anyway," Chu answered with a grin.

"The robe makes it easier, though," Hsu Ta grumbled.

Chu laughed. "It is our victory banner," he said. "It keeps the men happy."

There was one thing, however, that made the men mutter to each other behind their shields. Even Chu, they felt, could not perform the miracle they would need when they got to the wide Yangtze River. They were close, and they would have to cross to get to the north. If the crossing were not swift and the army had to wait on the open mud flats, it could be readily attacked, especially if some of the large, heavy Mongolian warships were nearby.

Chu, quick to sense the feelings of his soldiers, sent word through his officer corps.

"No one is to worry about the crossing. Let each man do exactly what his commanding officer tells him, and all will be well."

"A fine message," said Chu grimly to himself, as the army reached the Yangtze and peered with anxious, superstitious eyes at the broad, swirling waters. He examined the river. The water surged restlessly. Each time it broke against the bank, it cast an ever higher line of foam upon the mud. Rivers flooded cruelly in the Middle Kingdom, and this one seemed about to display a terrible temper. Already it looked as if the waters would soon be lapping hungrily close to the army. In such a case, the men would panic and flee. No wise soldier or farmer ever stayed to tempt the anger of the River Dragon or the souls of the drowned, ever reaching for more victims.

There was a warning silence among the men as they peered at the river through the swirls of evening mist. Astride Black Dragon, who nervously pawed the ground, Chu stood high in his stirrups with his sword arm raised. As if by a miracle of will, he held the men quietly behind him. He gave no order, and he kept his face turned away so that any who wished to run might do so without losing face in his eyes. His faith made them patient. Even when the waters lapped at the feet of those in the front ranks, not a man moved.

And then, in a parting of the white mists like the pass between mountains, a fishing boat appeared. As the soldiers stared, there was another, and then ten, and a hundred more, some fishing boats, some broad, flat-bottomed barges two hundred feet long, many private pleasure boats with dragon prows and deep blue sails. There were sampans, net-fishing boats, seagoing junks with square sails of matting, and eight-oar boats known as wind-piercers. They came through the mists without a sound, answering the request Chu had sent by courier days before to every village, town, and city for miles around. They worked throughout that night and the next day, to carry Chu's Red Turbans, with all their horses, supplies, and war machinery, across the wide Yangtze River to the opposite shore.

When it was done, Chu gathered the elders from each village together and thanked them.

"Do not dishonor us by thanks," said the one they had elected as spokesman. "It is little enough return for what you do on our behalf."

"I was a farmer myself," said Chu simply. "I know what it means to take days from work in the summer months."

The waters continued to rise, so the army camped inland.

"The mists and the swollen river are a good omen," said Chu to Hsu Ta. "The Mongols will not suspect that we would cross the river at such a time. We begin this campaign with good fortune."

"May it continue in the next weeks," responded Hsu Ta. "Since you plan to attack all five Mongol fortresses along this part of the river at once, you will need all the gods in Heaven on your side."

"Not all five at once, Hsu Ta. Four at once, and then we meet at the largest stronghold on this side of the river, Anch'ing. Like Hao-chou, the siege of Anch'ing will take all of our strength and a good deal of strategy as well. Rumors must be spread of our dispersed attacks on the other four strongholds, so that they will not expect us in total force at Anch'ing."

"Why don't we attack each stronghold separately, one after the other?" Hsu Ta asked.

"Because of another lesson I learned from Genghis Khan. When he conquered eastern Europe, he did so with only one hundred fifty thousand Mongolian riders. But by attacking in several places on one day, and on the next day massing his army together again for a battle a hundred miles away, he fooled the Europeans into thinking he had five times as many riders as he actually had. Terror was one of his greatest allies." Chu smiled. "The whole of this province of Anhui will fall just as quickly, once we have broken through these five gates."

"Tell me what you want me to do," said Hsu Ta.

As Chu's retainers moved quietly about his large camp tent, serving a dinner of rice and fish and tea, Chu outlined the campaign. Chu, Hsu Ta, and two other able commanders were each to take twenty-five thousand men, two and a half regiments. Hsu Ta would attack the Mongol detachment downriver, the other two commanders would take posts upriver, and Chu would move against the mountain fortress above Anch'ing at Ch'ienshan. In exactly ten days, they were to meet outside the walls of Anch'ing to lay siege.

"Why do you look at me like that?" said Chu, noticing Hsu Ta's dazed expression.

"Three hundred years ago, the Sung Emperor had a militia force of seven million men. When the time came, he could not beat the Mongols in the southern provinces. Now with one hundred thousand men you propose to take the fortresses of a whole province in a few short weeks. You are possessed by the devils of insanity."

"You know better," said Chu quietly.

"Yes, I know better," said Hsu Ta. "But what I know has nothing to do with logic."

Before the sun had risen, while it was still dark, the Red Turbans struck camp without a sound, leaving nothing behind them. For several miles, whichever way they went, they rode their horses only through water and mud, which quickly covered their traces. Farmers and Mongol couriers reported that they had simply vanished. For the Chinese farmers it was the beginning of hope; for the Mongols, the beginning of terror.

Just before daylight, Chu spoke to the twenty-five thousand men in his detachment.

"We have ridden upriver far enough. Now we go north to the mountains, to Ch'ienshan, but we will not ride

together. In the way I have taught you, you will move in
groups of no more than twenty men, vanish, and reappear
at the base of the mountain gorge marked on the maps
of your officers. Throughout, and most especially as you
near Ch'ienshan, make no more noise than the wind."

With these words, and knowing that his men would
obey him completely, Chu wheeled around on Black
Dragon and led off his own handpicked group of one
hundred mounted advance archers. He wanted no more
for the preliminary maneuver he had planned. He also led
a spare horse, with a large bulging sack draped across
its back.

It was the middle of the sixth month, and the heat was
intense. The horses kicked the dust from the road into
steaming air, and not a cloud was visible in the burning
blue of the sky. The men were drenched with sweat in their
leather armor; and shields, swords, lances, and bows grew
slippery in their hands. The horses panted as they made
their way up the steep, winding trails of the foothills. But
though the men gazed longingly at the shade cast by willow
clumps and thick pines on either side of the paths, they
begged no rest. Chu, at the head of his column, did not
look back. No man should know the humiliation of being
watched, lest he weaken and flee. Leading their horses
over the steepest of ridges, the men panted desperately
in the heat, but not one left the column.

That night they rested gratefully beside the trail, but
they rose the following morning before light. Again it was
a hot day, but by noon they had reached the mouth of
the gorge. They had now come to the place of danger.
If they rode up the center of the gorge, they would be seen
by the Mongols in their watch towers on the huge stone
fortress that guarded the top of the pass on the mountain

ridge. If they deployed and rode through the forests on either side of the pass, they would doubtless fall into carefully laid traps of overhanging boulders or prepared avalanches of stones or logs. The men looked up at Chu and awaited his orders.

Chu scanned the foothills and with practiced glance picked out the small groups of converging Red Turbans.

"We are ready," he said, and began to open the large sack that had been draped across the spare horse he had led for the past two days. The men had noticed that an evil smell came from the sack, but none had questioned Chu. Now, from the sack, he pulled out twenty objects, so hideous that even the most toughened rebel looked away in disgust. Into each object, Chu poured a small amount of liquid and sealed the hole with wax.

When he was finished, he said, "Twenty among you will each take one and mount it upon the end of his lance; then follow me."

What the Mongol watch beheld riding toward them up the gorge twenty minutes later struck such horror in their midst, that in panic and confusion they did not immediately attack. Terrified, they clambered to the ramparts. For, before their eyes, bearded human heads, bleeding and grimacing in the agonies of death, moved toward the stronghold. Each head was mounted on the tip of a lance and came forward in a cloud of evil-smelling smoke, which spewed out of the severed necks. The heads actually seemed to be drifting toward them supported on nothing but a swirling gray cloud. What frightened the soldiers even more was the fact that the heads were those of slain Mongol soldiers.

"Ride faster," Chu ordered his archers.

Under cover of this hideous form of smoke screen,

which created confusion and fear in the Mongols and made them lose one precious minute after another, Chu's archers reached the base of the fortress wall.

"Now, *shoot!*" ordered Chu.

Quickly the men tore the hideous, grimacing heads from their lances, mounted the heads on strong arrows, and drew their bows taut. The heads were shot in a single volley over the wall. When they landed on the other side, they smashed open and the full extent of the noxious gas was released, to fill the fortress with cloudy, poisonous vapors.

"Over the wall, hurry," Chu cried.

Rope ladders and grappling hooks were thrown, and in two minutes Chu's men had scaled the ramparts and dropped down the inside of the wall.

"The gate!"

The vapors were beginning to clear as Chu's men fought their way through the few Mongols that had sufficiently kept their wits about them to resist. Chu's attack had been too abrupt and too horrifying, and the Mongol officers of the gate had lost control of their men. Chu's archers swung open the heavy doors. A few seconds later the Mongols recovered, and those still inside the building dashed out with raised swords. They were ready at last, but it was too late. The gates swung fully open, and thousands of Chinese rebels poured into the court from the gorge below. In the pitched battle that followed, every Mongol was slaughtered. By evening, the fortress of Ch'ienshan belonged to Chu.

As he ordered the collecting of all arms, horses, silver, gold, and rice, Chu waited impatiently for couriers from the other detachments. Toward evening of the following day, two riders came up the gorge and later that night, two more. The other strongholds had also been won, and the armies were preparing to march on Anch'ing.

The attack on Anch'ing, a large walled city built near a lake fed by the Yangtze River, was an open attack. The four armies came together and rode on the city in close order behind Chu and Hsu Ta.

"They'll be expecting us?" said Hsu Ta.

"The Mongols have been waiting for us ever since they got word about the attacks on the four other strongholds," Chu answered.

It was true the Mongols of Anch'ing expected the Red Turbans. But they had expected a contingent of twenty or thirty thousand, not an army of one hundred thousand men. Chu smiled as he thought of it. There was no time to call for auxiliary troops, even if the Emperor should agree to send them. The general had a hundred thousand men, but many were Chinese who had been forced into the army by being starved off their farms. Their loyalty could hardly be trusted on a battlefield. Without the Chinese, the general had barely forty thousand troops. He could not attack, and he did not dare to be sieged into starvation. Chu did not envy him.

"Look," cried Hsu Ta, as the Red Turbans galloped across the fields to the walled city.

Chu saw at the same moment and he knew a fury unmatched by anything he had ever felt before. The western gate of the city had been swung open, and the drawbridge let down across the moat. Out of Anch'ing rode the Mongol cavalry to fan out in three ranks in front of the walls. On the saddle of each Mongol soldier, a Chinese citizen had been placed as a protective shield—not just strong young men prepared to fight and die if necessary, but old men and small children, whose screams of fear Chu could hear across the field. The Mongols had armed themselves with an impenetrable living shield.

"Barbarian pigs," spat Chu, but the calling of names was useless now. He raised an arm to halt his men, and as he did so, the fury on his face subsided.

"Dismount, throw down all arms except for the short dagger in your belts, and crawl," said Chu to his officers. "Give the order instantly."

And to show his men what he meant, Chu leaped from his horse, threw down shield, lance, bow and arrows, and sword, and fell flat on his stomach. Quickly he began to crawl toward the Mongol ranks, moaning the words of surrender at the top of his voice.

Angry at such a public display of humiliation, even if it should turn out to be another of Chu's tricks, the men nevertheless obeyed him, and in a few seconds, tens of thousands of Chinese soldiers were crawling unarmed to the feet of their enemy.

A murderous hail of Mongolian arrows felled nearly a thousand Red Turbans, yet the pain of death was less to them than the loss of face.

Chu crawled grimly forward. "Don't stop moving," he ordered. And then at the top of his lungs he again cried the words of surrender.

"If you wish to surrender, halt," returned the Mongol general loudly.

By that time Chu and the first rank of his Red Turbans had nearly reached the horses of the Mongol archers. Under the guise of making an elaborate kowtow, Chu flung himself at the horses' feet.

"Kill the horses," he muttered swiftly, and faster than the wind, his order was carried down the line. With a thrill of pride, the Red Turbans understood. All sense of humiliation vanished in the prospect of yet another victory.

Before the Mongols realized what was happening, the knives of the Red Turbans had slashed, killed, or wounded the front rank horses of the Mongol archers. Then, as if by command, each Red Turban in the front row grasped a hostage and carried him toward the drawbridge. As the old men and the children fled back into the city, the second rank of Red Turbans attacked the dismounted Mongols and created as much confusion as possible, while the Red Turbans in the three rear ranks raced back across the field for their own arms and horses.

Hand-to-hand combat began in earnest. The glitter of swords and the cries of soldiers filled the air. Cutting and slashing in every direction, the Red Turbans created complete havoc in the Mongol army. Chu moved like lightning among his soldiers. He seemed to be everywhere, shouting encouragement, leading attacks, forming and reforming groups, and riding to head off fleeing Mongols wherever they tried to escape. One band of Mongols headed for the drawbridge to hide behind the city walls. But Chu wanted no return to the city, where innocent Chinese might be hurt. He shouted to Hsu Ta, and the two, with a contingent of cavalry behind them, rode to the drawbridge and fought the Mongols back.

"Stay here and close the gates, so that no Mongol can get back in," Chu ordered the men who fought on the bridge.

A few minutes later, the drawbridge was pulled up, and the city gates clanged shut. The Mongols, trapped outside their walls, were finished. Nearly all were killed in battle. Those that remained, Chu executed, in retaliation for their having used Chinese children as hostages.

As the Red Turbans rode victoriously through the streets of Anch'ing, Chu saw an arrow wound in Hsu Ta's arm.

He had been hit in the rain of arrows while the Red Turbans had crept toward the horses.

"Forgive me, my friend," said Chu.

Hsu Ta shook his head. "No forgiveness is necessary. It is because you love the children of China that men follow you. And because they follow you, we will rid China of the Mongols."

"You make it sound so simple."

"It may be war is simple. But I know one thing that is not. A woman." Hsu Ta pulled a letter from the purse at his belt. "This came yesterday. It is from Ma Hou."

The Moon Gate

I N N A N K I N G, Kuo was dying. Behind the serpent-embroidered curtains on the great four-poster red lacquer bed, he lay twisting the silk sheets between his fingers and listening to the priests as they chanted prayers for his soul. Across the room, over his clothes chest, was a picture he liked to look at. It was of a mountain, which vanished at the top into floating mists. A small, lonely man climbed the mountain, but the strange thing was that, depending on the light in the room, sometimes the man seemed lower on the mountain and sometimes higher. Lying by himself in his room for long hours, Kuo had developed an illusion that if ever the man should reach the top of the mountain, on that day Kuo would die.

Today the man on the mountain seemed to stand lower than usual, and Kuo wondered if it was because today he expected Chu to arrive. The thought of Chu made Kuo feel more lively than he had felt in weeks; and as if to force himself to concentrate only on life, Kuo turned his glance away from the picture toward the latticed windows that looked out on the private family courtyard.

There sat his wife in her usual place under the plum tree. Around her, the young children of his concubines played and cried in the sunshine with their nurses. Maids sewed and washed vegetables and rice in the pool. Neighbors came in to gossip, street vendors and merchants came in to show their cloth, jewelry, brasses, and other wares, and Madame Kuo's closest friends sat and played Mah-Jongg all day. It was a bright, gay scene, for Kuo had commanded, despite his wife's protest, that life in the Kuo mansion go on undisturbed. How good a thing was the family in China, with its prescribed order. Each person knew his place and his duty to the whole, and in this way, all were made safe and happy.

When Kuo looked around again, his daughter Ma Hou was standing quietly by his bed.

"Please, Father, let me tell them to be less noisy in the courtyard. Or let me have you moved into my own court, which is more quiet," said Ma Hou gently.

"There is little time for life, but much for eternity. Let me enjoy my family, child," said Kuo. "Soon enough my name will be written on a soul tablet and placed in the ancestral hall, and I will have enough quiet then. Tell me now. Does all go well in the house, First Daughter?"

While it was true that Madame Kuo was *Tai-tai,* First Mistress of the Kuo mansion, it was to his clever and educated daughter that Kuo entrusted much of the management of his affairs. There were many relatives of several generations, servants, and children sold into the Kuo household as apprentices by peasants who could no longer afford to feed them. All these had to be looked after, clothed, and fed. And then there were the accounts, from Kuo's business in medical supplies, from the family grain fields, and the household books. Ma Hou kept all in perfect order. She had done so while Kuo fought with the Red Turbans, and had continued to do so while he was ill. Young Kuo was less clever. It took all his energy to struggle through his studies with the house tutors.

"All goes well in the household, Father," said Ma Hou.

"Then why does that child cry so," said Kuo. He had been listening to a small girl-child wail on and off for days, and it saddened him. "Can nothing comfort her?"

"That is the daughter of Third Uncle. Her feet have lately been bound. I remember from my own childhood that the pain is bad for the first few months, continues for a year, and then lessens afterwards. But when she grows up she will have Golden Lily feet, and no man will be ashamed to have her as wife. So do not upset yourself over the matter, Father."

"Bring a chair," said Kuo. "I want to discuss other things."

Ma Hou nodded to her maid Apricot, who carried a small gold painted chair to her mistress and placed it near the bed. "Now order the ginseng tea for my father and leave us," said Ma Hou.

When Apricot had left, Kuo turned his face once more toward the bright scene in the busy court. His glance clung to the life beyond his latticed window as if to support his own failing heart.

Ma Hou rested her hand gently on the sleeve of his sleeping robe.

"Don't be concerned," said Kuo. "I shall live until Chu Yuan-chang comes to see me. Are you certain you sent the letter?"

"You know I sent the letter. And you know he sent

word that he would come today," answered Ma Hou.

Something in his daughter's voice made Kuo turn to look at her. Ordinarily, he would have teased her a little, but because he was dying, he did not want to waste precious minutes.

"You have seen Chu and you love him, is that not so, First Daughter?"

"Yes, Father," said Ma Hou. She blushed faintly, but her voice was clear and firm.

"Another woman would have lowered her eyes in shame to admit such a thing," Kuo grumbled, but his tone was affectionate.

"I am not another daughter. I am the daughter of my father," said Ma Hou. She smiled.

"Not only shameless but impertinent as well," said Kuo. He sighed, and an expression of sorrow filled his eyes. "Do you guess something of the future and what it will mean to be the wife of Chu Yuan-chang?"

"He is a great man."

"He is more than a great man," said Kuo. "If the Red Turbans succeed in raising the standard of revolt throughout China, Chu will be greater than a man. They will make him the Son of Heaven."

"What of Han Lin-erh?" asked Ma Hou. She knew well, from political discussions with her father, that Han was Lord Liu's favorite.

"In the great peasant uprisings of China's history, it was the favor of the people that granted the Mandate of Heaven to the new ruler. The people do not love Han Lin-erh."

"Nor do I," said Ma Hou quietly. "He was always a cold man, and now that he has found a passion, it is for power."

Kuo was surprised at the accuracy of his daughter's judgment.

"But do you also know what it will mean should Chu be placed on the Dragon Throne?" asked Kuo.

Ma Hou raised a hand, the fingers long and pale as delicate onion shoots, to straighten a gold lacework butterfly that ornamented her hair.

"It means that I shall be lonely, because an Emperor must also take secondary wives and concubines. It means that Chu will change through the years, because a man cannot remain as he is if his power extends over sixty million people. It means political intrigue and danger to me and the children I will bear, because always there will be enemies. But you see, Father," ended Ma Hou, with a small, happy sigh, "there will also be Chu."

"You are an idiot," grumbled Kuo.

"Yes, Father," said Ma Hou.

"I will arrange it," said Kuo.

"Yes, Father," said Ma Hou.

"He is here!"

The cry was raised by the servants at the main gate and carried through the entry court and the main hall, along the corridors to the east and west wings and back to the inner courts. Everywhere, menservants, maids, children, and three generations of relatives ran excitedly about with the news.

"Have you seen him?"

"No. But someone said he was bigger and broader than ever."

"I had a peek at him. He looks far too elegant for a soldier."

"Well, he could hardly ride through the streets of Nanking on his black horse, in his armor and red robe. The Mongols would spot him and kill him in a minute. There is a price on his head high enough to buy all the silk in Suchow."

"He has an angry face," said a child.

"The anger is not for you," explained an older Fourth Cousin, "nor for any Chinese. His anger is against the Mongols."

As Chu strode through the halls and courts of the Kuo mansion, his heart pounded. Was she there? Did she wait for him beyond the moon gate in the court of the Red Chambers? Or while he was in battle had she been betrothed to Han and been removed to a place beyond his reach.

But he dared not think of such personal matters. His first duty was to Kuo. In her letter, Ma Hou had written that her father was dying, but that his soul would have no peace unless he saw Chu before he died.

A servant, finding it difficult to keep up with Chu's long stride, scurried quickly along the corridor to the verandah outside Kuo's room and managed just barely to announce Chu before he entered the bedchamber.

As Chu greeted his old friend, he worked hard to keep his face from showing the shock he felt. It was hard to believe that the pale, wasted man in the silken sheets had once been his fat, cheerful, dirty companion in the marshes and on the battlefield.

"No need to pretend," said Kuo crossly. "I know perfectly well that I look like a ghost from the underworld."

Chu smiled in relief. At least the bellowing voice was the same.

"Have you got any rice wine with you?" asked Kuo, his eyes gleaming hopefully. "They give me nothing but this horrible ginseng tea."

"A thousand pardons," said Chu, with a low bow.

"Then get the chessboard and my box of cash from that table over there. If I cannot drink, at least I can be allowed the pleasure of gambling a little as we talk. Good. Set the board on my bed. You may have the white stones. Now, tell me the war news, and then there are things I wish to tell you."

While they made mock battle with the game, Chu described in detail his maneuvers against the five towns north of the Yangtze River. Kuo's eyes glittered with pleasure.

"But still, you do not play chess as well as I. See how I've beaten you? You owe me a hundred ounces of silver."

"A hundred ounces?" Chu exploded. "You know perfectly well I haven't—"

Kuo's pale face suddenly grew serious. "But you have."

He reached beneath the small painted wooden head pillow and drew out sheets of thin rice paper. Silently, Kuo handed these to Chu to read. "If you agree, sign. I have no time to waste on go-betweens and geomancers and lawyers. We will simply call a few witnesses to countersign the document. Do you approve?" asked Kuo as Chu quickly scanned the sheets.

"I realize that we ought to have the proper go-betweens and soothsayers to match your dates of birth and choose lucky days for all of the ceremonies, but I am afraid I have very little time left. I simply wish to make you my adoptive son, to give you, with Young Kuo and my secondary sons your share in my estate, and to see you, if she does not displease you, married to my daughter Ma Hou. I have listed in those papers all the property, ingots of gold and silver, and the cultivated fields that are to be yours, and the furniture, hangings, jewels, and the country villa with its lands and gardens that are Ma Hou's dowry. All you have to do is tell me whether you are willing."

The only words Chu heard clearly were those that meant he could marry Ma Hou. For a moment, he was too breathless to speak.

Kuo's laughter bellowed through the room. "Like my daughter, you are an idiot," he said.

"Yes, Adoptive Father," said Chu, ducking his head awkwardly to hide his embarrassed happiness.

"You also have my permission to place soul tablets for your own parents and for the Fang Chang, whom you promised to honor, in the Kuo Hall of Ancestors," said Kuo graciously.

When the papers were witnessed and signed, Kuo seemed weaker but more at ease in his mind. He sat quietly back among his pillows. "I have one or two matters more to discuss with you. I shall mention them now, as it not likely we shall have such a good opportunity again for a quiet talk. First, the matter of your rival. I do not speak of Han, whom you will handle as you think best, but of Chang whose power grows at Lake Tung-ting in Hunan province and also in the province of Hupeh, and who now marches east through the province of Kiangsi. My guess is that he plans to keep going until he takes Hangchow. If he takes Hangchow, I think he will refuse to acknowledge Lord Liu, and will separate from the Red Turban cause entirely. Already he calls himself Prince Chang and makes delays in sending tribute rice and money to Lord Liu. He is a man without honor and is greedy only for himself. Be careful of him, Chu."

"You are wise," said Chu. "I will remember."

"Another thing. When I die, Lord Liu will make Han Lin-erh Generalissimo in my place. He will offer you the position of Assistant Generalissimo. Refuse. For the time being, permit Han to do the ruling from whatever city Lord Liu chooses. You keep the army and go on fighting."

"Again you are wise," said Chu and kept his face solemn. Had Kuo forgotten that this had been Chu's policy for a long time? That Chu had already made this decision back at Hao-chou?

"I know that the object of our cause is not to conquer and rule small kingdoms, but to recover all of China from the Mongols," Chu said. "Do not worry. I shall not forget what you have said."

"Then if you know all this," Kuo retorted crossly, "why are you sitting and listening to an old man give unwanted advice when you ought to be laying siege at the moon gate?"

Chu rose so quickly that it made Kuo laugh.

"But you had better bathe first," warned Kuo. "You will find the women in my house perfectly ridiculous on the subject of water."

In the soft summer evening, Chu went quietly to stand in the shadow of the round moon gate. Under the dusky blue-green sky, dances were being held for everyone's entertainment. Festive lanterns had been hung under the eaves on three sides of the court, and small tables of tea and sweetmeats had been set outdoors where the ladies sat along the verandahs chattering and enjoying the spectacle. A small orchestra of flutes, zitherns, several pipas, pipes, and drums sat in one corner of the court, while the dancers, their long sleeves fluttering in the light breeze, performed first the slow dance "Drooping Hands" and then the faster "Snapping Waists." The fragrance of sandalwood incense burning somewhere in an inner room mingled with the scent of the peonies in the court. Chu found the scene altogether entrancing, and instead of immediately announcing his presence, remained in the shadow of the round gate to watch the performance until it was over.

He really saw very little of the dance. The figures moved
before his eyes as if he were in a dream, because beyond
the dancers in the center of the verandah sat Ma Hou. In
her rose pink jacket embroidered with a pattern of mandarin ducks and a deep purple skirt, which lifted just
enough to expose her tiny, silk-slippered feet, Ma Hou
seemed to Chu to possess all the pale, delicate beauty of
the Moon Goddess. Her hair had been freshly curled and
filled with golden hair ornaments, and thin gold bracelets
circled her wrists. She spoke very little throughout the
performance. Now and then, she leaned against the verandah railing. Her dark clear eyes searched the court, but
not finding what she wanted, she sat back, frowning slightly
and fluttering her fan. When first she did this, Chu laughed
silently in delight. He was certain she looked for him. How

beautiful she was and how lovely that she loved him as he loved her.

Still he waited. He stood until the dances were finished, until the court had been cleared and the ladies retired. When her maids had left for the night and Ma Hou lay alone in her moonlit chamber, Chu crept forward. He entered softly from the verandah and stood near her bed-screen, enameled with peacock feathers and nightingales. The room had been perfumed with jasmine, which mingled with the orchid scent Ma Hou used in her bath. Chu trembled to hear her soft breathing and could move no further.

"You mustn't stand there like that. You are either to come in or go away." Her clear voice broke into his thoughts like the sound of golden bells, and she had used again the very first words she had ever spoken to him, three years before.

"You will frighten him off with that bold tone," said her old nurse crossly, whom Chu suddenly saw sitting in a chair across the room. But this time the nurse followed her words with a laugh, knowing that all had been arranged between her young mistress and Chu.

Chu grinned at her in the darkness and remembered too his own first words. "Only small men mind boldness in a woman," he said. "And as you can see, I am anything but small." With which he pushed away the screen and stood before Ma Hou.

"I am not worthy," he whispered.

"Nor I," she whispered in return, with her flower hands against his chest and her clear eyes raised to him. "But I will try to make you happy, Chu Yuan-chang."

He held her fiercely, protectively, and she trusted him with all her heart.

On the next day they were married. Token betrothal presents were exchanged, the ritual cups of rice wine were sipped by the bride and groom and guests, and then, though there had not been the usual elaborate wedding procession with the presents carried through the streets of the city and the bride heralded by singing girls and musicians as she rode in her red wedding litter, Ma Hou was nonetheless brought to Chu in a red wedding chair wearing a red bridal veil. They kowtowed to Heaven and Earth, one another's ancestral tablets, and to Kuo and Madame Kuo as their parents, making vows of filial piety. Seeds, beans, cash coins, and fruits were scattered outside the main gates for the city's children, and within the mansion, presents of money were given to all and a great banquet was held.

Not for one moment could Chu take his eyes from his bride in her beautiful wedding robes, and it seemed a long time to him before finally, in the newly decorated rooms in the eastern wing, which for now was to be their home, they were at last alone.

They were happy for two months.

Then, one day, Kuo looked at his picture, and seeing the small man disappear into the mists at the top of the mountain, he drew a last breath and died.

For Chu and Ma Hou there were the complicated details of an enormous and formal funeral to handle. Dozens of distant relatives and mourning guests came who had to be fed, entertained, and attended to. There were monks and priests who needed rooms for their services and incantations, for the burning of spirit money, paper houses, horses, and for the other various offerings of food and incense. There was material to buy for white mourning clothes and the ordering, according to family precedence, of the mourning procession that was to accompany the coffin to the family graveyard.

And then, as if all this were not enough for Chu and Ma Hou to bear after so little time together, a courier arrived bringing a message from Hsu Ta.

"You must come back. Lord Liu has set up Han as Generalissimo of your recovered city of Anch'ing. They wish to make Anch'ing the capital city of a reestablished Sung dynasty. Even Brother Wang, with militants from the White Lotus Society is here and supports their agreement. I am worried about the army. Come quickly."

"You must go," said Ma Hou when she had read the letter.

"But there is the funeral. I can't bear to leave you with all this worry," said Chu.

"I can manage," said Ma Hou. "And remember, our father and I have made many friends for you in Nanking. You can count on the people here whenever you should need them."

"What a treasure you are," said Chu.

"Yes," said Ma Hou, smiling at him. "Remember that, and also to bathe."

"You sound like a wife," said Chu in mock scolding.

"I am," Ma Hou sighed happily. "Yours."

Southern China
is Ours

WHEN CHU ARRIVED at Anch'ing, he saw immediately that Hsu Ta had been right to send for him. In the few months of Chu's absence, all had fallen to the devils of chaos. Liu had divided the Red Turban army.

In a rage, Chu stormed about his camp tent outside the walls of Anch'ing, listening to what Hsu Ta had to tell him.

"After all your efforts at organization, the Red Turbans are once again bands led by warlord chieftains. Some of the bands Lord Liu has taken north with him to Anhui's capital Hopei. His aim is eventually to invade the province of Honan and take the old Southern Sung capital K'aifeng for Han to rule."

"But that brings him near the Yellow River, into North China! Is he mad? We are not ready yet to take North China," exploded Chu.

"There is more. The rest of the army is scattered in every direction, east and west along the Yangtze, and to the south. They were released by Liu to fight the Mongols and liberate the towns in any way they choose. In fairness, he left you fifteen bands, about twenty thousand men," finished Hsu Ta with a wry smile.

"And if I take these men to fight, who is then left to protect Han and his reestablished Sung dynasty," said Chu bitterly. "How could Lord Liu have so completely destroyed all those years of careful planning! As a Confucian scholar, he should have applied the rule of the Family, that to be strong there must be unity."

"I think in part it was the influence of Brother Wang," said Hsu Ta. "When he arrived last month with his White Lotus fighters, he advised that Han and Lord Liu go back to the old way of scattered attacks. He also advised giving Chang, who now calls himself Prince, more freedom to fight in his own way. I don't understand," Hsu Ta sighed. "It's all so stupid."

Chu stopped short in his angry pacing about the tent to stare at Hsu Ta. "But I understand. It is Brother Wang's ancient hatred for you and me. He would do anything to destroy my influence. And since Han wants power, and Lord Liu supports Han, it was easy for Brother Wang to persuade them to disperse my army. Lord Liu must be getting old not to have seen that in weakening the army, he takes away Han's power and that of all the Chinese people. You are right, Hsu Ta. It was a stupid thing to do. Come now. We will go to Han Lin-erh at Anch'ing and see if it is possible to reason with him."

It was not possible.

Once again, as before in Hao-chou, Han had established himself in the greatest mansion of the city, setting himself in a regal position above all the city officials. This time, however, Chu discovered as he paid the customary polite visits to local officials, things were much worse. Because Liu had invested Han with the title of King and had announced that he was to inherit the mantle of the Sung dynasty, Han made greater exercise of his power. All of the rules of liberation that Chu had laid down, Han had ignored. Rice fields had not been restored to the peasants. Taxes had not been lessened. Courts of justice had not been reestablished. The contents of storehouses and granaries held by Mongols or the rich Mongol-supporting Chinese had not been divided among the poor. There were still no plans to put the system of examinations back on a fair basis so that all—not just the gentry families—might have a fair chance to earn the honors and salaries that came with the reward of a degree. And there was still inflation. No attempt had been made to fix the coinage on a proper basis. Every political ideal Chu and his Red Turbans had fought for had been betrayed by Han.

Sickened by the realization that he had been betrayed, Chu went to Han's mansion the following day. If Chu had not been so angry, he would have found his reception amusing. There sat Han, not in a chair at an ordinary table, but on a gold-lacquered throne on a raised dais placed at the end of a long Hall of Audience. He even wore a gold ceremonial robe embroidered in five colors with serpents and, on his head, an imperial gold cap surmounted with a board from which hung twelve pendants.

What was not amusing was the thickly fleshed figure standing next to him, whose eyes under the scarred, shaven crown stared with hatred as Chu approached the dais.

"Why have you turned a revolutionary army back into plundering bandits," demanded Chu after performing a perfunctory kowtow to honor the symbol of Chinese rule if not the man. "Why has there been no attempt made at proper government? If we go on in this way, there will be nothing but anarchy in China, and the Mongols will find it an easy job to retake the territory we have gained."

"That is only your opinion," said Han in his smooth cultivated tone.

Chu stood for a moment watching the expressionless face of Han. The eyes were opaque. One could not see beyond the flat surface into the depths of Han's eyes.

"Our opinion—if I may speak of *our* opinion, Venerable Lord," began Brother Wang with a deep bow to Han, who nodded briefly to give permission, "—our opinion differs from yours. We feel that for a time it may be to our best interests to divide the troops and let them take territory in all directions. And as for proper government, we do not feel as you do that all should immediately be set to rights. If King Han is to be strong, he must make the people feel his power a little before giving everything away." Brother Wang's voice was smooth and flattered Han, but his glittering eyes held the laughter of triumph as he stared at Chu. "It is King Han's wish, as you most probably have guessed, that you and your troops remain outside the walls of Anch'ing to protect his throne."

"I cannot. I must reorganize an army and begin again. If King Han wishes really to rule someday, instead of simply lording it over a small territory that might at any moment be taken from him, I must win it for him first. You have given your King bad advice, Brother Wang. It is my hope he will understand this one day."

Han's fingers, with the long nails now of idle days, paused in their tracing of one of the serpents on his robe. If Chu was not mistaken, Han had paled a little.

"You will leave me some protection?" His glance rested

on Chu's face, the eyes deepening somewhat as if to remind Chu of what had been and was still between them. An old friendship, the saving of a life in battle, and the taking of a woman.

"I will come to you whenever you need me," said Chu quietly. "And I will leave you five thousand men. Goodby, my lord."

As Chu left Han's Hall of Audience, the bitterness of his lonely fight overcame him. With Kuo gone, he had no ally, and against him were Liu, Han, Brother Wang, and Prince Chang. The Mongols in Peking, he thought grimly, must be laughing at him, thinking him a fool among fools.

They were not laughing, but the imperial court was indeed immensely relieved when their spies and couriers brought word of the quarrels among the Red Turbans. The Emperor Toghan Timur himself went so far as to remark, "See? How often have I told you there was no real need for concern. Our garrisons in the south can handle the situation without fresh troops. Now let us make ready to enjoy the Festival of Chrysanthemums. I shall want hundreds of potted chrysanthemums in my chambers."

It took Chu two and a half years, but finally, by the spring of 1356, he had raised and organized a new Red Turban army of seventy thousand men. With these men, taking advantage of the political preparations made by Kuo and carried on by Ma Hou and Young Kuo, he entered Nanking. Han was still at Anch'ing. Unfortunately Prince Chang had seized Hangchow. And Liu was still trying to lay siege to K'aifeng in the north. But at Nanking, Chu was secure. While he continued to acknowledge King Han as the inheritor of the Sung dynasty, Chu from necessity created a seat of actual government at Nanking to rule all the recovered areas of the south. Han had the title, but he did not rule. Chu cared nothing for titles, but he did everything necessary for the proper government of China.

At Nanking, Chu did all the things Han had not done at Anch'ing. Besides slaughtering what was left of the Mongol garrison and removing all Mongols from office, he weeded out any Chinese officials with records of corruption. He held examinations, and those were given office who earned it with the merit of their scholarship, not their purses. Granaries and storehouses were opened for all in need. The fields outside the city were restored to the peasants. Taxes were suspended for a period of a year. There was justice again in the courts. On two mornings each week, Chu made himself available in the Reception Hall of the Kuo mansion to all petitioners.

Hsu Ta was now the full commander, under Chu, of the Red Turban army. A permanent garrison protected Nanking, and the rest Hsu Ta led across the southern provinces of China like locusts ferried by the wind, liberating towns from the Mongols, distributing landlords' hoards of grain, and establishing loyalty to Chu wherever he went. The stories spread of these brilliant guerrilla warriors on horseback, experts at the surprise raid; the ambuscade; the night attack; the feint; the pretense of defeat only to attack again; the psychological use of noise, smoke, and terror; the sneak dawn raid, and economic blockade. So expert had the Red Turbans become at duping the Mongols, that rarely were many Chinese hurt.

While Chu carried out his military and governmental plans in the south, Lord Liu was still attempting the siege of K'aifeng in the province of Honan near the Yellow River. In 1358, he stormed the city and took it briefly, long enough for him to send for Han and set him up in this more important capital. The situation lasted less than a year. As Chu had foreseen, the time was not yet ready for the reconquest of the north. The Emperor Toghan Timur sent fresh troops in time, and by 1359, K'aifeng had again fallen into Mongol hands. Han and Lord Liu were forced back to Anch'ing.

For five years, Chu improved his position in the south and along the Yangtze River, with Nanking his well-fortified capital and stronghold. His red robed figure astride Black Dragon was a familiar sight in the streets of the city, and the citizens of Nanking were proud of him and grateful.

"People talk about you everywhere," said Ma Hou, smiling at her husband over the satin slippers she was embroidering for their second son.

Chu looked at Ma Hou in mock severity. "Have you been out again in your sedan chair? It seems to me I did see your chair behind the spirit screen near the front gate this morning, now that I remember. Has no one ever told you it isn't proper for a woman to leave the house so often? I thought I had married a well-brought-up young lady, and you behave no better than an ordinary coolie woman."

As Chu spoke, he waited for the sound of Ma Hou's laughter. Her voice and the sight of her delicate loveliness always filled him with joy. She had given him two sons and a daughter in these years, and still she was as beautiful and slender as a young girl.

"For the King of Beggars, raised on a poor farm, an ordinary coolie woman is good enough," Ma Hou retorted.

Chu burst out laughing. "I ought to have you whipped with the heavy bamboo, you know that, unworthy female."

"Unworthy female!" cried Hsu Ta, entering the family court where Chu and Ma Hou sat under the plum tree in the place Madame Kuo had sat before her soul tablet had been placed near her husband's in the Hall of Ancestors. "*Tai-tai* is such an unworthy female that without her help, we could not so easily have taken Nanking. Good morning, First Mistress," said Hsu Ta, bowing low in his affection and esteem for Ma Hou.

Chu and Ma Hou smiled at their closest friend, glad always to see him and to receive him safely back from battle.

"You look thinner than ever," scolded Ma Hou. She turned to her maid Apricot. "Stop making moon eyes at General Hsu Ta and bring food."

It was true, thought Chu. Hsu Ta looked thin and worn. So small his friend was, yet so full of energy and devotion. Chu remembered suddenly the old days, when even the task of resewing Chu's robe had not been too menial for Hsu Ta.

It was Ma Hou who realized that Hsu Ta had something of importance on his mind, and when the food was brought and served to the men, she took up her embroidery and left them.

"It is time to face the problem of Prince Chang," said Hsu Ta abruptly. "My couriers inform me he plans to attack Han."

"I've been prepared for the possibility," Chu answered. "Now that we have pretty well recovered south China from the Mongols, it is not surprising that Prince Chang should want to assert his power. Always in the past after a rebellion against the Throne, warlords arose who tried to divide the country into small kingdoms for themselves. But they did not always succeed, nor shall Prince Chang. China will be one."

"Under Han?" asked Hsu Ta.

"Under Han," Chu replied firmly.

News of Prince Chang's siege of Anch'ing came on the fifth day of the fifth month, the day of the Dragon Boat Festival. It was the third big festival of the year, a day when pestilence and evil spirits were most to be feared, the day of evil animals, like the wasp, toad, snake, scorpion, and centipede. Everyone wore lucky charms and bought branches of peach, willow, and pomegranate, and papers in the five colors as protection against epidemics, and hung blossoms of yellow mugwort, arranged in the shape of tiger heads, above their doors. There were entertainments, outings, and parades of dragon-boats on all the lakes; but still it was a day of ill omen, and everybody remembered it.

"Fate is strange that I should receive this message from Han on such a day," Chu said to Ma Hou, coming into their chamber. He held out the paper for Ma Hou to read.

"Prince Chang's bandits camp beneath our walls. You promised you would come if I should need you." It was signed "Han" and stamped with his seal.

Chu himself led the Red Turban army, with Hsu Ta at his side. This time there were two differences. He rode the son of Black Dragon, now too old for war. And he took Young Kuo to ride with him, as he had once ridden with Kuo himself. The boy was less able than his father had been, but under direct orders made an excellent captain, and his devotion to his brother-in-law Chu was plain.

Chu's army rode on Anch'ing in five ranks. The first two ranks were heavy cavalry in full leather armor for protection in close combat. The three rear ranks wore only helmets, and their horses too were without armor. They were the archers and the javelin throwers, for whom lightening speed was the greatest weapon. Each man was fully armed, and for each trooper there was a spare horse, herded behind the columns with the wagons of heavy siege equipment, food, and supplies. This battle was to be no ambuscade, no swift night attack, but a conquering force that would not stop until all south China was unified.

At Anch'ing Prince Chang's army waited for them beneath the walls. Beyond the walls, flames of fire licked the heavens and black clouds of smoke billowed against the blue of the spring sky.

"*Aiya!*" cried Chu, his eyes black with rage. "He has destroyed the city of Anch'ing. He will pay for this if I have to hound him for the rest of his days. Why did not Han send word earlier?"

"Probably he could not have imagined that Chang would destroy the city," said Hsu Ta.

"Also, probably more bad advice from Brother Wang," said Chu. "Give the order for attack. Instantly."

At the order, the three rear ranks of light cavalry galloped forward between the ranks of heavy cavalry to let loose the first barrage of javelins and flaming arrows. Chang's army was thrown into chaos, and those unhorsed dashed madly about in fear and confusion. Many fled, taking rapidly to the woods and the fields and whatever boats they could find to cross the marsh waters and the lakes nearby.

"Where is Chang?" asked Chu, racing to fight by Hsu Ta's side. Hsu Ta as usual was in the thickest part of the battle, his scimitar flashing among the bellowing horses and the screaming men. The noise of steel, horses, and men was so intense that Chu had to shout to be heard.

"I have not seen him. I don't think he is here," Hsu Ta

shouted back. "Watch out. Your back is unprotected."

Chu wheeled the son of Black Dragon and cut down the three men behind him, slashing their necks with his huge sword. He raced from one section of battle to another, shouting orders, arranging counterattacks, reforming scattered groups, and commanding the forward advance of the heavy equipment to scale the walls.

By evening the battle was over. Thousands of Chang's men lay dead in the fields, thousands more had fled. At no time had anyone seen Prince Chang.

Within the city of Anch'ing, all was disorder. Many citizens had been murdered, tortured, hung by their necks from chains, or been made to suffer the death of a thousand cuts. Most of the houses were burned to ruins, and there were still fires and smoke in every direction.

"Why!" cried Chu, enraged beyond belief.

He came upon Han, crouched frightened in his throne room, unattended and entirely alone. He was no longer the cool, proud man Chu had known.

"Why!" Chu demanded again.

"Brother Wang," Han whispered, staring at Chu out of frightened eyes. "He has joined Prince Chang. He betrayed me to Chang, to fight you."

"Where are they?"

"When they had killed Lord Liu, they fled to Lake Po-yang. Chu, they have destroyed my city, my capital."

"Why did they leave you alive?"

"They did not mean to leave me alive. I hid," said Han, cringing. "And when your advance was reported, they did not want to be found here. They thought they would do better to fight you at Lake Po-yang."

"Very wise on Chang's part; his strength is in the central provinces and in Hangchow in the east. But it won't last

long. I shall destroy him," Chu said, his jaw clenched in fury.

"Don't leave me," Han begged. "Take me with you."

"Come then," said Chu. He strode from Han's throne room, and Han scurried behind.

Chu escorted Han back to Nanking and gave him a small villa on his own grounds near the Lake of Cranes. Rarely afterwards did he leave the villa, but spent his time reading the Classics and writing poetry according to the seasons. Now and then Ma Hou brought her children to visit Han, but very little cheered him. He sat silent and alone. He had failed; he was a man without face.

Such as they were, a broken body thrown from the ramparts of Anch'ing, the remains of Lord Liu were sent to his relatives in Peking. His courage and wisdom had founded the Red Turbans, and Chu honored him in death.

With little pause, except to establish Han at Nanking, Chu and Hsu Ta moved on to Hangchow.

As they approached the city, Chu grinned at Hsu Ta.

"Remember the first time we came to Hangchow?"

Hsu Ta laughed. "What ragged beggars we were. And look at us now, in armor and silk robes, with an army of tens of thousands behind us. That was fourteen years ago. We've been fighting a long time, Chu."

"Tomorrow morning we fight again. There is Hang-chow."

Rose-pink clouds of sunset glowed over the lovely, ancient southern capital, and Chu vowed to capture it without destroying it. After a carefully planned siege, which lasted two months, he did so. In the next two years, Chu also mastered the entire Cantonese region of the south, as well as Chekiang and Kiangsi. The one area he

did not hold in south China was that around Lake Po-
yang, once the stronghold of the Red Turbans and now
infested with the bands of Prince Chang.

It was just after New Year in 1367. The marshes were
cold, and the winter mists drifted across the watery mud
flats.

"We will not attack in formation," ordered Chu. "Tell
the men to fan out. Many of them know this place well,
from long ago. Hsu Ta, take ten regiments and attack the
mountain fortress. Be careful especially of the Peak of the
Twin Swords. Do you remember the traps, all the overhanging boulders and avalanches of logs?"

"How could I forget them," Hsu Ta replied. "We were
here a long time."

The two men rode together at the head of their soldiers
a little longer. The men made no noise, and the only
sounds to be heard were the lonely calls of the geese
through the hanging mists. To the south, the rocky gorges
and silent mountain cliffs were also still. When the men
came nearer to the village, surrounded by its lake of reeds,
and saw the fortified walls of its central fortress, Chu gave
a quick nod to Hsu Ta who cantered off leading his regiments toward the mountains. Chu would lead the attack
on the walled fortress ahead.

"Dismount," he ordered, "and leave the horses here."

He led the men on foot, guiding them surely through
the baffling marshland of hidden creeks and paths and secret waterways. The fens were treacherous, but not to
those who knew them as the Red Turbans did. It grew
dark, and as the men crept forward toward the village, they
heard the sounds of drunken brawling, sounds they had
once made themselves, before Chu had taught them to be
an army.

"Advance Archers, forward," whispered Chu, and his officers passed the order among the men.

"Flaming arrows, immediately," said Chu, "before we are seen from the watchtowers."

In less than three hours, Po-yang was taken. Prince Chang's bands were in no condition to hold off the Red Turban army.

It was a shock to Chu to see what Prince Chang had done to Lord Liu's lovely Palace of Coolness. In the large spare halls, the glazed brick tiles were cracked; and though the sandalwood pillars still gave off a faint fragrance, they were scarred and marked. No exquisite scrolls of calligraphy now hung on the walls; in their place only garments and pieces of armor thrust upon pegs driven into the plaster could be seen. Porcelains lay broken, and screens were flung down. Hangings were torn, and clearly the gold and silver ornaments had been melted down. Only the library remained unharmed, and Chu gave orders that Lord Liu's books should be sent to the newly opened schools of Nanking.

Prince Chang himself was not in the Palace of Coolness. Chu's men found him drunk in a village wine shop and dragged him before Chu. Bearded and filthy, he flung himself at Chu's feet.

"So this is the son of a fisherman who was clever enough to grow wealthy in the salt trade, raise the standard of revolt, and successfully fight Mongols for fourteen years. This is the Master of three provinces, the man who captured Hangchow and Soochow." Chu's expression and voice were flat.

"Yes, Venerable Lord, all that," cried Prince Chang, hope flickering in his eyes.

"Stand up," commanded Chu. "I want to see the man

whose bands have rivaled the Red Turbans all these years."

"I am not at my best," murmured Prince Chang, struggling to his feet.

Chu examined the filthy jacket and trousers, and the cringing, shamefaced man before him. "You were an able warrior. It is too bad your cause was your own, not that of China."

"Don't kill me. It was not I who burned Anch'ing or killed Lord Liu. Don't kill me."

"I will not kill you. I will permit you to save your honor by killing yourself." Chu signaled for Young Kuo who stood near. "Take an escort and return to Nanking. Tell my wife all is well. I leave the city in your charge and hers until I return. Also, take this Chang under guard. Permit him to commit suicide when you reach Nanking, but only after all see him in chains. And now," said Chu, "where is Brother Wang?"

Hsu Ta entered the hall carrying a box, which he placed on the table before Chu. "Forgive me for depriving you of the pleasure, Chu, but considering the beating he gave me all those years ago at the Hua Shan monastery, I hoped you wouldn't mind if I attended to Brother Wang myself." With these words, Hsu Ta lifted the cover of the box. The hideous grimace on the decapitated head made it clear that Brother Wang had not died without pain.

"And now," said Chu, "the central provinces are ours as well. All China south of the Yangtze River, together with the provinces of Anhui and Hupei is Chinese, liberated from Mongols and bandits alike. Sleep well tonight, Hsu Ta. Soon we march north."

The Last
of the Mongols

I N   T H E   N O R T H E R N capital of Peking, which the
Mongols called Cambaluc, the Emperor Toghan Timur was wakened as usual in the dark hours of early
morning.

"It is time for Morning Audience, Your Majesty," said
the Chief Eunuch, head of the imperial household, as he
directed the servants with his fat, jeweled hands to feed,
bathe, and dress the Emperor of all China.

Toghan Timur groaned. "Why does the Audience always have to be so early!"

"It is the hour fixed by the Board of Astrologers according to the stars," answered the Chief Eunuch, as he had
answered every morning for thirty years. The Emperor
had never liked to get up. There was always the same
struggle.

"I never hear anything very important anyway," complained Toghan Timur, sitting up in the great bronze bed. He reached for the bowl of his favorite green tea.

"That's because you don't listen," the Chief Eunuch wanted to say, but instead he asked merely, "Do you want the camphorwood perfume as usual to scent your robes?"

In the Audience Hall, the court was restless. Frightening rumors had spread through the halls and courts of the Imperial Palace, and everyone was worried. The wide terrace in front of the Audience Hall was already filled with princes and ministers who had come before midnight to bring petitions and memorials to the Emperor. While they waited in the courtyard for his arrival, they separated themselves according to their rank and stood in groups together, each group beneath its own clan banner. The darkness was lit only by flaming lanterns in the lower courtyard. Within the Audience Hall itself, palace eunuchs moved lighting the huge horn lanterns, arranging their jeweled robes, exchanging low whispers.

No voice spoke aloud. No one moved in the courtyard; all faces were stiff and grave; all eyes gazed straight ahead. In the last moment before dawn broke, a courier blew his brass trumpet loudly, and this was a sign. The Emperor had left his palace, and his imperial procession was on its way, moving slowly through the broad lower throne halls, passing through one great entrance after another to arrive at the exact hour of dawn.

Now the couriers, the first of the procession to arrive, cried out together, "Behold the Lord of Ten Thousand Years!"

Behind the couriers came the Imperial Guard; and then one hundred bearers in yellow uniform appeared, carrying the Emperor's palanquin of heavy gold up the marble steps to the Dragon Terrace. There the Emperor got down from his carrying chair and, wrapped in his robes of gold embroidered with dragons, the imperial tasseled hat on his head, he went slowly down the Hall to the dais and seated himself on the Dragon Throne. As he walked, every man and every eunuch fell down upon his knees and shouted the sacred greeting, "Ten Thousand Years—Ten Thousand Years!" Each bowed his face upon his folded hands as he knelt.

Arising from this kneeling multitude, the Prime Minister went forward and then fell again to his knees before the Emperor. He began to read a memorial from a long scroll, which he held in his hands.

"Stand, you may stand," said the Emperor irritably. "I cannot hear a word you say when you kneel, you mumble so." This was the fourth Prime Minister in fifteen years. The first had frightened him so with his tales of rebels, that Toghan Timur had had him cut in half at the waist. Since then, Prime Ministers had been afraid to speak about the rebels very often, but it was soon evident, despite the delicate classic style in which the memorial was written, that this was the subject on the Prime Minister's mind.

"In the name of Heaven and Earth, say what you have to say," sighed Toghan Timur.

The Prime Minister trembled, but finally he stood, put his elaborately written speech aside, and came to the point.

"We must send for fresh troops immediately, Your Majesty. Send to Tamburlaine at Samarkand or to Toktamish for help from the Golden Horde."

"I won't. The last time I sent for troops, they did not go south to fight rebels. They fought each other, one group for my son and one for the old Prime Minister, right beneath the walls of my own Palace."

"I beg you to reconsider," said the Prime Minister, going down on his knees again. "A report has just been brought to me. The rebellion is no longer confined to the south. Chu Yuan-chang leads his Red Turbans north from the Yangtze this very hour."

"But I told you to have them stopped at the Yangtze River," said the Emperor fearfully.

"There were never enough garrisons in the south, Your Majesty," said the Prime Minister in sorrow. "But we still have time to protect North China, O Lord and Khan of the World," the Prime Minister wailed in his high voice. "Only send for troops."

A hush fell over the assembled courtiers in the Hall of Audience as they waited for the Emperor Toghan Timur's reply.

"This is the realm of your great ancestors, Genghis and Kublai. You must maintain it to the death," cried the Prime Minister.

It was the wrong thing to say. The minute Toghan Timur heard the word death, he rose from the Dragon Throne, turned pale, and whispered, "Make immediate arrangements. I leave Cambaluc for my northern palace of Shang-tu tonight."

The Morning Audience was over. No provision for his princes and dukes, no thought for his courtiers and eunuchs, no thought for the ladies who lived in the Palace of Forgotten Concubines! Of himself only, Toghan Timur thought, and of all that he had lost. With his favorite eunuchs and concubines, he started north, weeping as he passed through his beautiful North Lake Park with the Wall of Nine Dragons. As he passed through the Chu-yung Barrier Gate, which he himself had built in the Great Wall of China as a portal to the Western lands, Toghan Timur recorded his misfortunes.

"O thou, my great city of Tai-tu, decked with all possible conveniences!

"O thou, my costly and cool summer residence of Shang-tu. Through my sins has it come to pass that I have lost my realm.

"My Tai-tu, made out of nine materials of the noblest sort, and my Shang-tu which contains nine-and-ninety perfections.

"My lofty name and fame as Lord and Khan of the World.

"My sacred city of Tai-tu, gloriously built by the all-powerful Emperor Kublai! Neither in summer nor in winter did I ever experience sadness. All, all have been wrested from me!"

These words were all that Toghan Timur left those who had been faithful to him. He had refused to fight, and the court could only do its best to cover the flight of the Emperor north to Mongolia beyond the Great Wall. The last hope lay in covering up this flight and in putting up some sort of proud front. The people of the court were Mongols after all, conquerors of the world, who had ruled from Korea to Bagdad, from the steppes of Russia to the Danube.

Two hundred and fifty thousand strong, Chu's Red Turbans moved north. Each man was well horsed and equipped, and able to ride for weeks if necessary, in the five ranks of perfect formation. They thundered over the soil of China from the Yangtze to the Yellow River, recovering the provinces of Honan, Shensi, Kiangsu, Kansu, and Shansi. Wherever Chu led the Red Turbans, he sent couriers ahead with a proclamation summoning the Chinese to rise against the Mongols. As he had once said to the people of South China, he also said to those in the north, "These barbarians are created to obey and not to command a civilized nation."

And as in the south, the people responded with universal joy. In the north, too, the towns supplied money and opened their fortified gates. Everywhere, the Chinese had had enough of the Mongols. The northerners could hardly believe what was happening. In the south, the Mongols had ruled only for eighty-nine years. But North China had been in Tartar hands for two hundred and forty-two years; Peking itself for four hundred and thirty-two.

The army was near Peking by late spring.

"Do you realize how much territory we've covered in only three months," said Hsu Ta, "and without so much as a major battle."

Chu and Hsu Ta were cantering at the head of the army over the broad northern plains beyond the Yellow River. Spring came late in the North. The sky was a paler blue, and the northern winds, carrying loads of fine yellow sand from the Gobi desert, whirled in chilly gusts about well-covered heads. Here it was necessary to wear silk robes lined with fur long after the Spring Festival, and even caps of fur on the head.

"It's hardly been worth dragging the siege machinery and the cannon with us," Chu agreed. "It's been more like a military excursion than a campaign." He let out a great shout of laughter into the wind. "The terrible Mongols are paralyzed with terror at the sight of us," he said. "I roar, and they run." And urging his horse into a gallop, Chu rode as if to chase them even faster.

When the army reached a point twenty miles south of Peking, Chu reined to a stop and raised his sword arm to signal a halt. Then, before all the men, he made a low obeisance to his friend and greatest general.

"For all the years of loyalty and friendship, I give you Peking, Hsu Ta. Command the army and take the Northern Capital that your name may be written in the history books and your ancestors be proud."

"I will take it, Chu Yuan-chang, and lay it at your feet," Hsu Ta replied simply.

For a moment, Chu did not answer. He could no longer say, "It is for Han." Early in the year, quietly among his books and flowers, Han had died. Instead Chu said, "It is up to the people of China to confer the new Mandate of Heaven. They have suffered and fought and died, and it must be as they wish."

Again Chu bowed to Hsu Ta. Then he turned the son of Black Dragon's head and rode back among the ranks of Red Turbans, who parted to clear a path for their leader. Those in front who had heard the conversation between their First Lord and his Commanding General repeated it to those behind until all had heard.

It was then that the shouting began. As so long ago, when he had first ridden into the village at Lake Po-yang, Chu heard someone send up the cry, "Beggar Wang! Ten thousand years to our King of Beggars!"

But suddenly there was a hush, and another cry.

"Not Beggar King, Brilliant King! Behold the Lord of Ten Thousand Years, our new Son of Heaven, the Emperor of a new dynasty, the Brilliant, the Ming!" The army's shouts echoed over and over, as Chu rode among them, accepting their homage. He had not wanted China for himself to rule, but if China wanted him, he must accept. Everyone else—Han, Lord Liu, Kuo—who might have ruled was dead.

The First Emperor
of the Ming

B Y MIDSUMMER, Hsu Ta had taken Peking and
the army had crowned Chu Emperor of all China,
the Middle Kingdom, which is to say all of the truly civilized world or all the world that mattered. Chu's dynasty
was called Ming, meaning Brilliant, and he was given the
reign title Hung-wu.

"When you are dead," said Hsu Ta, "I will see to it that
you are also given the posthumous title of *Tai-Tsu*, Great
Ancestor."

"A thousand thanks," said Chu wrily. "I am deeply in-
debted to you for already being so busy about my death."

"Are you two quarreling again?" scolded Ma Hou, entering the Hall of Audience where Chu and Hsu Ta strolled
back and forth before the Dragon Throne of China.

"And you?" demanded Chu, grinning at his wife. "What
are you doing wandering about the Imperial Palace of

Peking as if you were still back home in the Family Court at Nanking."

"I wish I were," said Ma Hou. "I don't like this Mongol Palace."

"Nor do I," said Chu abruptly. "I intend to burn it, as I intend to burn every reminder that the Mongols were ever in China. Not a single Mongol palace, Mongol institution, or even a single Mongol will remain."

Hsu Ta and Ma Hou exchanged a glance. Chu knew that neither approved of this wholesale slaughter of Mongols, of the fact that he had ordered the Red Turbans to continue conquering outlying Mongol territories. But Chu could not forget his ancient bitterness, he could not forgive his enemies for the death of his mother and father and brother, and for the presence of Mongol horsemen on the ridge of the hills above his family's farm during all his youth. He had spent nearly twenty years fighting Mongols. He was not going to stop now.

But there was another reason. A sense of strength, a feeling that there was someone to lead and to unify and to govern wisely, were necessary to China now. Her spirit had nearly been broken by the Mongol rule, and she needed a taste of her own vigor to make her strong again.

"What is more," said Chu, "when matters are finished here in the north, I shall make Nanking my captial. We shall rebuild it, Hsu Ta, and make it beautiful. My son may rule from Peking if he wishes, but Nanking is my home."

"And the Great Barrier Gate to the Western lands?" asked Hsu Ta.

Chu leaned against a carved and lacquered pillar near the throne dais. He knew what Hsu Ta meant.

"It is the culture of the Golden Age of Tang, the Ancient

Classics of the Confucian scholars, the traditions of our glorious past I wish to revive," said Chu. "I have no interest in the Western lands."

"But what of possible scientific progress, or technology? Surely it could not hurt to learn, if there is something to be learned," suggested Hsu Ta.

"You sound like Han used to," Chu frowned. "And I will say the same thing to you I said to him. We know enough for our own purposes. And what is the use of scientific learning if it does not lead to harmony of the spirit. No, Hsu Ta. The westerners are barbarians and have no soul, no knowledge of truth or beauty of the spirit. Our own ways are best. China needs stability, not change. We must rid ourselves, not only of Mongols, but of the Christians and Moslems and all the foreign devils the Mongols brought with them. We will thrust the West back into the sands of the Gobi desert and from now on trust only ourselves."